AN ORDINARY V
GILLIAN EDW.
COPYRIGHT © 2015 By (

Cover design by JD&J book covers.
Printed by Biddles book printing.

ABOUT ME
AN ORDINARY WOMAN

When I was 27 I knew I was going to write a book. I knew what it was going to be called, and I knew the time to write it hadn't arrived yet.

I couldn't understand why things seemed to keep happening to me. I felt ordinary and as I looked around me, other people seemed to have their lives organised and sorted. I felt like I was always falling from one bad decision to another.

As I got older, I had an image of me as a grain of sand, and saw that I was rolling down a snowy mountain gathering more and more snow, and gathering more and more speed, and as I felt myself spinning downwards towards the bottom of the mountain I felt dizzy.

One day, when I was 38, my snowball hit a tree and burst open. I shook myself down, and walked away. I felt free and in control for probably the first time in my life. And so began the journey into living my own life and writing my book.

I hope this will be the first of several books about me and my life, and I hope you enjoy reading them. If you do, please write a review when you finish it.
I now work as a colon hydrotherapist and clinical massage specialist so if you want any more information on that please feel free to visit my website at: www.colonichealth.co.uk
Or you can email me at gillianedwards63@gmail.com.
(No spam please)

ACKNOWLEDGEMENTS.

More than anyone, I would like to thank my husband and
best friend Graham for all his support and love
throughout everything I have done and achieved.
I love you with all my heart.
♥
I would also like to thank every one of my friends
for giving me permission to use their experiences
for me to tell the stories.
Some names have been changed.

Thanks to author, Clair Delaney for helping teach me
how to publish and for recommending JD&J cover
designs who designed my perfect cover.

To Nigel, at Biddles for helping me bring my e-book
into paperback with lots of help and advice. I can't thank
or recommend you highly enough.

To Jacqueline for first nagging me to write things down,
and to everyone else for their encouragement along the
way and being part of my story.
You know who you are.

A special thanks to my stepmother Heather.
She has been a constant support and friend for over 30
years.

And finally, Christine.
For being my sister and so brave and courageous dealing
with M.S.

My Grandmother once wrote in an autograph book I was
given:
Make new friends but keep the old, some in silver, the
others gold…
It sums up how I feel about my friends.

Contents

PROLOGUE

I stood in the bathroom fixing my make-up. Next thing I was crying, how lucky, I thought to have so many friends who care about me. How lucky to have also one friend so special, Jacqueline........

And so here I am, wearing a beautiful evening dress, make up reapplied, hair just so ready to go down to dinner. I close the door to my room and head for the restaurant.

As ever, I am greeted by the staff with smiles and affection. They all come to me in turn to speak to me and attend to my every need. I have become a familiar face here now and I like to think of many of these people as my friends, indeed they are since some have been to my home, and I to theirs, even today the hotel receptionist has invited me to stay in her home whenever I like. This is no empty polite gesture on her part, I know she means it.

'Miss Skidmore, How are you this evening?' It's Mario, Maître D, and my other best friend. Drop dead gorgeous, and one of the loveliest people I have ever met.

'Bene' I reply,

'Sure?'

'Molto bene'

He pours me some wine from the bottle he provided for me on my first night of this trip to see him. It is one of the nicest bottles of wine I have ever had and very strong, which is just what the doctor ordered, almost literally since the doctor told me the best thing I could do at the moment is to take myself off somewhere to get away from it all. He gave me a sick note and I booked my flight. Two days later I was here, into the arms of my friend who would lick my wounds, give me a hug, listen to my trauma, and share with me the sense of peace and tranquillity that has become so important to both of us during the time we have known each other.

I eat my meal, which is as always, wonderful. I would expect nothing else, this is a first class hotel and the cuisine is always excellent. Later I wait for a call in my room to say he has finished work. I go to his room where we will decide either to go out or stay in and drink or talk or just stay quiet together. It doesn't matter what it will be, we share a companionable ease whatever we do.

This trip is different than all the other times I have been here, because I am feeling a bit battered and bruised. I need a safe and comfortable place to relax and recharge for me to pick myself up again and carry on.

A few days later, I arrive back at the airport, and the bus driver helps put my case on the bus. Rare help indeed and I am pleasantly surprised. I get to the stop at the airport car park where I am parked, ready to start facing reality again, and true to form it smacks me in the face. I go to the car and the remote key won't work. I use the key and am not surprised to find that when I try to start it, nothing. I go to the bus stop to press the button to summon help.

'No problem, we'll send someone out to you' I send Jacqueline a text.

'Just when you think it's starting to get better 'shit' flat battery, can I cry please?'

'Answer comes back 'what, on the battery or the car!' As always she knows exactly what to say and I laugh to myself.

As I wait for help to arrive, the bus I've just got off comes past. It stops and the driver asks,

'Are you all right?' I tell him my problem and he says 'don't worry I'll radio to say where you are. Go back to your car they'll be with you in a minute'

'Thanks very much' and I mean it. I am surprised again at the helpfulness that I don't expect. By the time I get to my car the van is there ready to get me started.

I am surprised to find that it starts first time and as he leaves me and I re-establish myself ready for my journey home, I realise the interior light is on. Relieved that this was what had caused the problem, I switch it off and turn on my music. Bugger! Code required, and I don't have it with me. Two and a half hours of driving in silence, apart from phoning Jacqueline about ten times in twenty minutes, due to the limited reception of the mobile phone, who goes off to the loo to talk, I mean listen, to me. Oh well, I'll just have to sing to myself. I set off and arrive home in just over two hours. Hope I don't get a speeding ticket through the post…

Feeling disorientated, as I always do when I get back from holiday, I have a gin and tonic, then another, then another. I never used to like gin or tonic, but I found if you persevere you can get used to all sorts of things.

Seven forty five, the phone rings, it's Jacqueline, 'what you doin' Skidmore?'

'Nothin' much. Why? Do you want to come over? I can't come to you because I've had too much gin.'

'Are you tired?' Actually I feel knackered, but would enjoy her company. 'Sort of, but you're welcome to come over.'

'We're goin' out.'

'I'm knackered.'

'Tough!' I know she means it and will force me to capitulate with whatever she has in mind for me. 'I'm not allowing you to be on your own tonight. You've got until nine o'clock to sleep and I'll be over at nine thirty-ish to take you out. You can sleep in late tomorrow.'

'O.k., but you'll have to phone me at nine to get me up.'

'Fine, call you later.'

I fall asleep almost immediately and the next thing the phone is ringing. Get in the shower and put your glad rags on. I'll be there in half an hour.'

'I'm knackered.'

'You can sleep tomorrow, no arguing, get in that bloody shower.'

'O.k. see you.'

Half an hour later I am showered and standing in my undies. Jacqueline arrives, takes one look at me and laughs uncontrollably. 'You look awful, I love it!'

'Thanks I feel like shit, I can't believe I'm letting you do this to me.'

'It's revenge for all the late night phone calls.'

'Fair enough' I get dressed, put my make up on and we go off to Worcester. As we drive we talk of the times so long ago it seems, but in reality is only a few months ago when we would drive to Worcester for a night out to people watch and have fun. Not bad for two nearly forty year old girls.

'If you knew how hard it was for me to get in the shower tonight you wouldn't have made me do it. I'm so tired the water hurt me like needles on my skin.'

'Ha ha, good, I'm really enjoying this.'

We arrive in Worcester and meet Kelvin and his friend for a drink. I really enjoy the evening and know she was right to drag me out. We get back and after talking on the drive for some time, we go into my house for a coffee and more chat.

As predicted, next morning I sleep late, in fact it's after twelve when I emerge. I can't face unpacking my case so I leave it. At four thirty I am ready to go out and take the picture Mario has painted for me to be framed. It's called "The Bridge of Friendship" featuring yours truly, Mario and Pinocchio. Then I go to see if my computer is ready. The shop is closed. No matter I'll go next week. I go home.

Next day, Sunday. Get up, do some washing, call Jacqueline, go over, we sit in the garden with a bottle of wine and salmon sandwiches. We put the world to rights.

'You're definitely coming to work tomorrow aren't you?' Jacqueline asks rhetorically.

'Yes' I reply 'I'm too scared of you not to!'

'Good, you've got to get back into it again, into a routine.'

'I know.'

Monday morning. I drag myself out of bed, not much change there, although the weight on my shoulders is heavier than normal. When everything is good, work is hard going, but the people I work with are nice and many have become like my family over the years as we have shared the traumas of each other's lives. I don't have that fear and I know they will look after me and keep watch over me. It's just the work that spoils it, and for me, at the moment, I have the world's most mind-numbingly boring job.

I arrive at work and it's like wading through a force nine gale up the stairs, along the corridor, through the door to my desk. I am welcomed by my friends and sit down. I go to make a cup of tea, all the time the voice in my head is screaming 'I don't want to be here' I feel detached and completely out of place. Problem is that like all of us, it pays the bills and it allows me to work part time due to my twenty-two years of 'loyal' service.

Like any institution it is familiar and offers a certain amount of safety, although the security it offered that used to be almost part of the job description has now evaporated. Welcome to the real world, trouble is there aren't queues of people wanting to join this organisation and in the sense that anyone who has been in prison for so long becomes institutionalised, so it seems are most of us. It's scary to think that I may not have the courage to cut this umbilical cord I have with Her Majesty's government in what we are now calling "Jobcentre Plus."

We have been called so many things since it started, let alone since I joined. I just never knew the glue would be so difficult to dissolve. However the calling to get out gets louder and having been back to college to train in massage and reflexology, and this term, Indian head massage, I feel at least I am trying. College has also opened up new aspects to my life that wouldn't have been there had I not done it. However I don't feel that this is what it would be like if I chose to retrain for a new profession. This, I think, is playing at it.

Not that I mean this with any disrespect to my tutors or the courses I have undertaken, I just doubt my ability, dedication, and concentration to persevere and succeed, particularly at written work for something really serious. On a practical level I have no such doubts, I can 'do,' that is what I am good at, and I know how to talk about it, I am eloquent, or so everyone says, it's just the essays, assignments and exams. That is where I feel weak and know I would struggle. So, as I write, I am in a dilemma but to do nothing is to resign and give in. It won't come and drop in my lap, I know that. If you want something to change you have to go and do it.

However, I digress. I go back to my desk and after warming my chair for an hour I go to see my boss. He has been very supportive to me and I thank him for this. We have a chat, or 'welcome back discussion' as it is bureaucratically termed. This is the government's way of showing care to its employees, whilst fulfilling its responsibility to deal with that demon 'stress' which might cost a fortune at a tribunal if they have failed to care for the workforce. Very reassuring that! Only problem is that if we have more than four days in six months off sick we 'trigger a file' about inefficiency. 'We don't doubt you are sick, but all this time off makes you inefficient'. Typical. Problem is that we swing from one unacceptable extreme to the other. Years ago, people took two weeks sick each year and no one batted an eyelid. Then someone noticed and formed a committee, set up a working party and made some rules. Revised, re-evaluated and some good old case law whereby a council got well and truly clobbered for damages (quite rightly) but everyone catches cold and I end up sitting here being welcomed back like it says in the book.

I return to my desk and don't quite know where to start. It's the end of the quarter and lots of checks to sign off with that piece of paper to sign to say you've done your job properly. Trouble is this piece of paper is hotter than the proverbial potato and will definitely be used against you when we see fit. If the whole lot went up in smoke, or more fittingly, down the great big pan, nothing would happen in the world to affect so much as even a grain of dust.

After a chat with my friend about what's been happening in the last two weeks since I've been off sick, I set about doing some checks. I see a couple of workmates and feel the welling up of tears as I speak. I return back to my desk and my mate says.

'You're not up to this are you. Why don't you go home?'

'I can't, Jacqueline will kill me!'

'Look, you've tried and you're not coping are you?'

Tears well up in my eyes again and are dangerously close to overflowing.

'Come to the conference room with me?' We go and I dissolve into tears. I know she is right. It's so disproportionate to what has happened but I am unable to take control of the tears. I also know from past experience that often rationality is completely useless, especially when it comes to emotions. If I don't listen to that inner instinct telling me to go home and give in to it for a while, it will just come and get me some other time, only worse!

She goes to get my boss and I apologise and try to explain how I feel. Impossible really, since I don't understand myself. He is very supportive yet again and I am surprised once again.

I find out later the contents of my 'welcome back discussion' because of course it all gets recorded for the records: 'I welcomed Gill back to the section she is feeling much better.' At the bottom of the form it says, '1.30pm, Gill is feeling unwell and has gone home.' I find this highly amusing.

As I get to my car I phone Jacqueline, 'Don't shout at me, 'I say. 'I tried but I just can't do it!'

'Don't worry, you have to deal with things your way, don't think you have to do what I would. You don't do you?'

'No, but I hoped I could just get back into it, but I couldn't, I'm going to the doctor's.'

'Where are you?'

'On the car park.'

'Have you eaten?'

'Not since breakfast.'

'Right, you phone the doctor for an appointment, and I'll meet you for a coffee in ten minutes.'

'O.k.' We go for coffee and two poached eggs on toast, each. This caused confusion in the café; did we want one poached egg on one round of toast, twice? Oh, right, two eggs each and two rounds of toast each. No problem. These girls are really splashing out, and two mugs of milky coffee, one each. Understand! The diet can wait!

I go home. Next morning I take myself off to the doctors. I hope they don't suddenly decide to strike me off as a patient who is too persistent and costly. Thankfully not and the young doctor says he understands how I feel. He says he had something happen to him six years ago, knocked him for six for a while but reassures me that the tunnel is not very long and the light is not far away. He tells me I am showing signs of depression but nothing serious. With all the other things that have happened recently it just got too much for me and he gives me a note for two weeks, and advice to use my time well.

'Don't sit and stare at the walls, get out and do things and you'll be fine. You might find writing it down helps. Come back and see me in two weeks and let me know how you're getting on. I hope you will be much improved.'

I leave the surgery and also leave a huge weight that has been welded to my back recently. I look at the note, 'Nervous exhaustion.' I start to cry. That's exactly it. That's exactly how I feel. The relief is overwhelming. I return home and phone in to work.

Two weeks pass. I have taken his advice. I firmly believe that when you go to the doctor, you must take your medicine, otherwise why bother to go? I also believe that the doctor can't really cure you. You have to take responsibility for yourself. The doctor is there to help and point you in the right direction, but is not there to take your illness away. You have to do that for yourself. Of course I am speaking in general terms and am fully aware of the specifics. But that is not what I am discussing here. During these last two weeks, I have slept quite a lot. I know that this is my body's response to stress and, I believe, my brain's way of responding to overload. 'You sleep, I'll sort out the rest!' I have been to college. It took a lot of energy to get me there, but I find it so relaxing and therapeutic to do, it helps me to unwind.

I've also seen some of my friends, spoken to them on the phone, and visited one or two. I've been to church, and generally tried to keep busy, but without pressure. Just what the doctor ordered!

Today I have been back to see the doctor. As I wait in the surgery I feel my heart rate increase.

'How are you?' he asks.

'Better' I reply.

'But?'

'But' I reply. 'I took your advice. I haven't sat around staring at the walls. I've got myself out and about.'

'But?'

'But I didn't realise how bad I felt until I knew I had two weeks to unwind and relief hit me. I am still struggling to wake up sometimes and....'

'And you don't feel up to fighting fit for work yet?'

'Exactly.'

'What do you do?'

Good question, I think! I tell him where I work. 'It used to be the Benefits Agency, but now we're Jobcentre Plus, and they are dragging us kicking and screaming into this new world.'

'I understand. You're not up to fighting talk yet are you? I'll give you a note for another two weeks. Come back and see me then and we'll see how you're doing.'

'I've decided to write it all down,' I said.

'What, how you are feeling?'

'Yes, but last year I made a life changing decision and went on holiday abroad on my own. I've had the best year of my life, until now, and my friend has been nagging me ever since to write it all down. I got myself a new lap top this week and I think this will be a good place to start.'

'Good idea, I did the same thing six years ago. It was very therapeutic. I read it a few times and it really helped.'

'Thanks very much' and I mean it.

On the way home I call to see Jane. I always seem to call there when I've been to the doctors. I tell her what I told him and that I am going to write the journal that Jacqueline has been nagging me to do for the last twelve months.

'Good idea' she says.

'I'll be back to aerobics soon.' I say.

'O.k.,' she laughs. It's a standing joke of how many excuses I can come up with as to why I am not going to aerobics. This is not to say I don't go. We have been going together for a long time and miss it when I haven't been for a few weeks, but I cheat and catch up again with the waveform treatment, which is really good.

During the evening I speak to Jacqueline on the phone and read to her that which is written so far. She laughs and remarks at my memory for detail. Later I talk to my sister on the phone and read to her the bit about work. She also works for the government, although is now almost a full time union rep. She says if she didn't know better she would have thought I had copied it out of a book! High praise indeed.

So here I am, as I write, absolutely up to date. Don't know what will happen next in my varied and troubled life. But I do know the story of how I got to this exact moment. Of course it is only my perspective and anyone commenting on events is bound to see it slightly differently, or in some cases completely differently. That's o.k. though. That's what makes us all individual and keeps this life so interesting to stay involved with. However, this is my story and it is an honest account from my eyes, no one else's.

ITALY

'I can't go abroad on my own.'

'Course you can.'

'I can't.'

'You can, you can't go on a walking holiday in Wales or the like.'

'What about a health farm?'

'Absolutely not! You can do that any time, that's not a proper holiday. Now get to the travel agents and don't come back until you've booked a holiday abroad!'

I'm talking to Jacqueline. I've just found myself alone and haven't had a proper holiday this year. I really enjoy my holidays and am desperate to go away. I am entering a new phase in my life and know that although I have friends that I could go with, it's not only the wrong end of the summer when most people have made plans or already been away, I also know that I have to do this alone. I've never been on holiday on my own and am absolutely petrified. However, like most things in my life, I will hold my breath and jump in at the deep end saying a prayer as I leave terra firma.

Funnily enough, I remember when I was a child and dad took my sister and me to the swimming baths to teach us to swim. I can't remember how old I was but probably five or six years old. He turned his back for a moment and I was on the top diving board ready to jump. A sign of my life to come? Sometimes I perform a perfect dive (although not often!) and sometimes, well most times it seems, I land a spectacular belly flop. Ouch, it always hurts, knocks the wind straight out of me, but never quite kills me off! And of course, I soon get your breath back; the smarting fades and I go and have another go.

I go to the travel agents. The girls in there know me now and are always friendly. A cynic would say, 'they would be, they want your money' and they would be right. But I also think that these girls are more than that and have more interest than that, particularly the girl who always books my holidays. She has the top sales for

17

the company, and rightly so. Excellent at her job, she knows her customers and knows what they will and will not like. She freely gives advice and scrupulously checks details. Nothing is too much trouble and always with a smile.

I tell her my situation, and ask her if she has any ideas as to what I could do. 'I thought about a walking or some kind of activity holiday, 'I say.

'Hmmm.' She has a look through a few brochures. Nothing really suitable. 'I know just the thing, she says 'Italy!'

'Arrgghh, I can't go abroad on my own' that feeling of deja vous runs through my mind. It's easy for them to say, but they're not the one's doing it!

'How long have you known me?' she asks.

'A few years.'

'Do you trust me?'

'Yes.'

'Italy. I know just the place' I make vague protests and we go on a tour of Europe looking at other countries and hotels and debating what I could do there on my own. Eventually it's make my mind up time.

Deep breath. 'O.K.'

'It's a four star hotel, I wouldn't recommend you go in anything less. They will treat you beautifully. The food is excellent so you won't have to go out on your own to find somewhere to eat. You can dress for dinner, which you'll enjoy, there's a piano bar so you can go and have a drink and read your book in comfort after dinner without feeling out of place. They have a swimming pool and it sits right on the lake so you can swim in the lake if you want to. Transfers are included so once you have got yourself to the airport, the rest is organised for you.

We book it. They have a room for me. The flight goes from Birmingham on Saturday. Today is Monday. I have deliberately given myself as little time to prepare as possible so that I haven't got too much time to think about it and fret. At the end of the booking one of the other girls comes over, smiling eagerly.

'So where are you going then?'

'Italy' I say, and burst into tears, half with relief and half with fear.

'Oh, I'm really sorry' she says, 'I didn't mean to upset you.'

'Don't worry I'm o.k. Just feeling emotional' I go back to work, it's late afternoon and only a few people are left. 'Guess what I've done! I'm going abroad on my own, to Italy.' Just then Jacqueline appears.

'Good 'she says. 'Bloody activity holiday, you must be jokin'!'

On my way home I call to see Jane. 'I've done it' I say proudly 'I'm going to Italy.'

'Good,' she says. 'You'll love it. The Italian people are so friendly you've made the right choice.'

'But I'm terrified, what if no one speaks to me?'

'Just take a good book and soak up the sun, you'll be fine. I wish I could do it'.

Jane has been on holiday on her own years before and had no such fears as me. Somewhere between my mother, sister and best friend, we have known each other for years. 'Do you want a lift to the airport?'

'Yes please.'

'No problem.'

I go home, don't quite know what to do with myself. So many things to do and sort out. I pour myself a drink or two to calm my nerves and then start to get excited. The worst that can happen is that I'll get there and no one will speak to me, in which case I will just read and get a good suntan. What if the weather is awful? I'll read in the hotel lounge or at worst my room. What about eating alone in the restaurant? I'll take my book down with me or a newspaper and if it's too awful I'll just order room service and eat in my room. It's only for a week and the rest and relaxation will do me good. O.k., no problem, I am a grown woman. I can do this.

A few weeks before, my sister Christine had been to have her make up done in the make-up department of a shop somewhere. It looked so nice I thought I would do the same sometime. I went one Saturday with Jane and her daughter to Boots and walked around the make-up department. I was looking for colours that I like. I settled on the Estee Lauder counter and asked the lady to do my eyes in pink and grey. I couldn't believe the transformation.

During the week before I am going away, I go to Boots and ask the lady to do my face for me. 'I'm going on holiday alone, and need to make an impact!' I tell her.

We choose some colours and she shows me the latest way to apply my make-up. You wouldn't think that at thirty-eight years old I would need to be taught this skill, but strangely you do forget and fall into a routine that you never really think about. Newly beautified and feeling rather like a big pampered cat, I emerge with my goodies. Expensive, but essential. I always thought that expensive make up was a con but have now realised its benefits. Especially when you sleep in it, (how naughty is that!) and next morning find it hasn't slipped down to your navel during the night! It also seems to last for ages. So now I have justified my extravagance on make-up.

Saturday arrives, I'm packed, no mean feat since I have only had six days to do it. I have cleaned the house from top to bottom. Why? Why is it that we feel we have to clean the house before we travel? Is it because we want it to be tidy in case we are burgled or the pipes burst? Do we think our house is going to be taken over by a community of spiders, earwigs or worse? Or is it some psychological aspect that makes us want to take maximum benefit of our relaxation and coming home to a clean house means we are uncluttered mentally and physically, ready to start another clean sheet in our daily lives? Who knows, and do we really care? Probably not, but we do it anyway. Although, as I have travelled on a regular basis of late, I don't feel the need to perform this ritual like I once did. I have also refined my packing technique and am now able to do it in an hour or so.

I spend the night before my holiday at my sister's house and next morning she takes me over to Jane's house where my chariot awaits. We are all excited and she leaves me with a smile, a hug and a promise to keep in touch.

Jane makes me a cup of tea. Jane always makes me a cup of tea, and is always, without exception, available to me. I'll tell you about Jane later, but for now, we get into the car. Luggage, passport (checked at least 37 times) credit card, currency and tickets.

We arrive at Birmingham airport. Jane, Jodie, (her daughter aged 11,) and me. I am starting to look forward to this. We check in, I have a window seat so that I can look out of the window if someone unfriendly sits next to me. Then we go for a coffee, up to departures where we wander around the Body Shop. Jodie buys some body lotion and promptly hands it to me as a gift. A lovely gesture and very much appreciated. Then it's not too long before I go. I walk back to the car with them and we say our goodbyes. We both get a bit moist eyed. 'See you in a week' we say, and then they go, and I go, to gather myself, alone.

I watch the traffic for a while busying itself around the airport terminal, I wonder where everyone is going, how their lives are being influenced by this airport today and wonder if I am the only one travelling on holiday alone for the first time, nervous and full of anticipation. I find I am suddenly feeling very calm and uplifted as the sun shines and the aeroplanes fly overhead with their human cargo. I'm ready. I go through departures and wait for the flight to be called, trying to look calm, controlled and sophisticated.

We get on the plane and take our seats. I am sitting next to a middle-aged couple who start to talk to me. Where am I going? Why am I alone? Oh, aren't you brave going on holiday alone. I tell them a bit about myself and confess to being nervous. I tell them I feel a bit like Shirley Valentine and this is what people have been starting to say to me.

Next thing we are hurtling down the runway, full flaps, full throttle. I love it. I love the feeling of all that power and always feel the expectation of what awaits when we return to the ground.

Two hours later and we are coming down again. We land and the door opens. The heat and the smell permeate the cabin, and again this is something that always makes me take a deep breath. It's almost as though while I am in the aircraft I am still in the land I have left. I never feel that I have changed location until I smell the air and feel the change in the temperature.

The couple I have been sitting next to tell me where they are staying and say if I feel lonely, have any problems or need any help to call them. This is a lovely gesture and I thank them very much.

The air smells warm and dry. I walk across the tarmac, through customs, and collect my luggage. I go through to arrivals and find the rep who ticks off my name on a list and points me to coach number six. Actually it's a minibus. I get on, the driver takes my luggage and I wait for the others to arrive.

After around half an hour we are ready to go. Around a dozen of us. I am the only one alone. We leave the airport and I see for the first time the land of north Italy. Very dry and vineyards everywhere. What else did I expect? I don't know. I try always not to expect anything, that way you're never disappointed. This doesn't just apply to travel, I also apply this to other aspects of life.

The land changes and I start to feel more comfortable. Eventually I see the lake as we travel from place to place depositing our cargo to their hotels and apartments. Do they share my anticipation of what awaits? Will the accommodation match up to the brochure's description? Will the area they have chosen fulfil all their dreams? I hope so, for them and for me.

As we get nearer I talk to another couple. They are going to the same place as me, but a different hotel. We arrive at my hotel first and I disembark. I have been told this is the best hotel in this area. I hope so but, of course, it always depends on your own definition. I always have a mixture of feelings when I arrive at a new hotel. Usually I see some things that I really like, mixed in with some things that I'm not sure about.

I book in, hand over my passport, and am whisked off to my room. I always hate this bit, because it always feels to me like walking into somewhere with no personality. It takes some effort and energy to make it homely and comfortable and personal. So, out comes the luggage, neatly folded, hung up (hoping that all that tissue paper has done its job and nothing is too badly creased) and then into the bathroom to see what treasures await. Towels, (hope they're soft) Yes. Tissues, great, (I have left instructions that they must accompany me in my coffin, such is their necessity to my life) Cleanliness? Yes, along with a certificate to say the toilet is sanitised. Hairdryer and it works. The plugholes, will the water take all week to filter its way down? No, the water disappears instantly. I am satisfied so far. There is just one more check. The view. This is a single room and I am expecting the worst. I open the shutters and window. Surprised, no stunned. The view is one if the best I've ever had. Out across the lake, unobstructed and below me the pool. Great!

I call Jane. Got here safely, so far so good. Am going to get ready for dinner. Call you soon.

I call Christine. Got here safely, so far so good. Am going to get ready for dinner. Arrgghh! Dinner!

'Chris what am I going to wear?' I have brought most of my wardrobe with me, but which of these garments are suitable for a woman on her own, going to dinner in a four star hotel, for the first time. Will the inmates dress up or has smart casual taken over. Not that this matters normally. When you are with someone else, it doesn't matter. But alone I don't want to make a faux pas.

We discuss at some length. Want to fit in, but being alone I decide I need to either become mouse like

23

and be completely invisible, or go for it big style and knock 'em dead. Guess which I choose? Deep breath, in I go. Please God, don't let me belly flop!

We decide on a sort of compromise. Bright colour but not too outrageous. Cropped trousers, matching jacket and very high gold sandals. (Very sexy, if you like that sort of thing!) The shoes are very deliberate since I know I can't walk very quickly in them. This will make sure I don't gallop, and hopefully make me appear calm and elegant to watching eyes.

So, make up perfect, I descend the stairs and go to the restaurant. There is a girl there to escort me to my seat. I take my place and wait. Whilst I wait I scan my surroundings. I am uncomfortable. This table feels wrong. I feel like I am on the M6 at rush hour. It is not private enough for me and I am surrounded by other tables. I feel I need a wall behind me to offer protection from whatever may be going on behind my back. I can't relax properly. I check to see how these people are dressed to make sure I have got it right. I have. There is no one in shorts. The men are generally in 'smart casual' and the women are similarly attired. It seems that the dress code is smart casual at least but I feel you can dress up as much as you want, if you want.

The waiter comes and welcomes me. I choose my food and ask for his recommendation from the wine list. (Tip from Christine) I eat slowly and carefully, believing all eyes are on me. (Woman alone over there, wonder why?) Of course this is not strictly true, but I find out later there are a lot who do notice and think this. I silently thank my mother for teaching me polite table manners at a young age, and whilst I have never really felt the need, as now, to practise this art, my memory has not let me down. Eat slowly, take the food to your mouth, not your mouth to the plate, small portions at a time, chew properly with your mouth closed, swallow, pause, and don't gobble! Heavens! I had forgotten how much there was to this regular task! I decide not to have a sweet since this involves walking into the middle of the restaurant to help yourself and I haven't quite got the confidence for that tonight. Maybe tomorrow.

I finish my meal. I am one of the later diners to finish and the restaurant is quieter now. I ask the girl who showed me to my seat if it is possible to have a table on the terrace. She goes to fetch the restaurant manager. He sees I am alone and maybe senses my discomfort. He goes away and comes back with a table plan. Yes, there is a table free on the terrace tomorrow evening and I can have it.

I return to my room and call Christine. We discuss the 'meal experience' and then my next battle plan. "The Piano Bar"

I have decided that I must 'do the whole thing' and this includes going to have a drink, alone, in the hotel's piano bar. I will take my book and go down. I can read quietly and have a brandy, then retire to bed when I've had enough.

I take my book, nothing too taxing, it's "Bridget Jones Diary." Little do I know I will almost become Bridget during my stay here, well somewhere between her and "Shirley Valentine!"

I go into the piano bar, a lightening scan of the room and I spot my place. Near the piano, (I have my back to it) near the bar, and near the door. I can see what's going on and have my escape route planned if necessary. I sit. Fully aware of my posture I position myself into what I consider looks relaxed, comfortable, composed and confident. I wait.

Shortly, a young man arrives and asks me very politely what I would like to drink.

'Brandy please'.

He goes and returns with a brandy and some nibbles. I thank him and start reading. Well, that's not strictly true. In fact, I look at my book and see the words, but do not digest. I turn the pages at regular intervals and know I look as if I am completely absorbed in my task. All the time though I am watching with my peripheral vision everything that is happening. I drink my brandy.

Still not completely relaxed, I have another. My comfort improves and I start to relax inside.

At around eleven thirty I retire to bed. The worst is over. I have some more new tasks to perform, but am now starting to feel more confident in my new environment, and hopefully will now start to enjoy myself. Good grief! I almost forgot that. I have come here to enjoy myself. I sleep peacefully.

Next morning, I wake quite early, get up and dressed (another decision on what to wear but this time I decide without a call to Christine!) and go to breakfast. Breakfast tables are a free for all and you sit wherever you like. I decide to go outside on the terrace to eat in the fresh air. It's beautiful and with only six feet between the lake and me I can hear the water gently lapping the wall and even without touching it can feel its softness. It's like velvet.

Breakfast is a different ritual. The waiters bring you coffee or whatever beverage you desire, the rest is up to you which involves me going in to take my pickings from the big table in the middle of the restaurant. I feel more at ease now and whilst still being aware of my poise I get my food. Not too much since I am not very hungry: Some cereal and bread and jam. (Anxiety is still not very far below the surface.) I eat and then go back to my room.

At ten thirty I go to meet the rep. Not something I normally do, but as instructed by my travel agent I go. 'Tell them that you are on your own and they will tell you whether the trips you want to go on will be suitable for you. They will also look after you.'

I arrive at the front of the hotel and meet the rep. The couple that were on the bus are also there and stand with me. We are taken on a tour of the town. It doesn't take long as the 'town' really consists of this hotel and now a few other hotels that have grown up around it, along with a few bars and restaurants and some shops. The shops are exquisite as is usual in Italy. We end up in a bar where we are all invited to have a drink while we listen to all the 'must see' trips and events that the reps will earn their commission on.

I decide that whilst I am here I really should go out and decide to go to Venice and to the Dolomites. I fill in my form and hand it to the rep. Unfortunately, I have come without my credit card, since I didn't realise we were going to go for a walk. She tells me not to worry, Michael, here, is my rep in the hotel, and will be in the lounge tonight. I can pay him then.

We return to the hotel and I go up to change. My new bikini and matching robe adorn me. With my new straw bag, I put in my book, water, and t-shirt and head off to the pool. I find a sun bed and take my place. The weather is fantastic, thirty-four degrees. Hot, but not unbearable. I read for a while, and then fall asleep. I wake and once I find my bearings again decide to go for a swim in the pool. It's lunchtime and a lot of the people have drifted off to eat. I swim for a while and then go to the outside bar for some water and to ask about some lunch. They give me my water, but say the tables are full at the moment and could I come back later. I go back to my sun bed and drift off. I decide not to go for lunch. I'll wait for dinner later, or go into the town if I feel hungry later this afternoon.

Around six o'clock, I return to my room and take a shower. The sun has warmed and coloured my skin and I look healthy. I already had a tan, and although I know it's not good for you, I always feel better with a colour in the summer. I am lucky in that I really do not burn, and I always cover up when I feel my skin is getting too hot.

Phone call to Christine, which becomes a daily ritual we both enjoy. I tell her of my day, and we discuss what to wear to dinner this evening. Feeling more confident, I decide on an ivory shift dress, Italian, as it happens, and a very feminine ivory devore over shirt, along with the gold sandals. Make up to match, i.e.; gold and bronze.

I go downstairs slightly earlier and take my credit card so that I can pay for my excursions. I walk along the long corridors, up the few stairs and along another corridor that leads to reception and the lounge off to the left.

I walk in, the room is beautiful. Very large, square and colonial. The floor is wooden parquet. There are fresco's on the ceiling and magnificent, glistening, chandeliers. The furniture is sympathetic to its surroundings and befits its setting, with complementary newspapers hanging in the middle. It could be the nineteen twenties, in fact, it was. This room has changed little since those times and has stood the test of time with classic elegance.

I see Michael, sitting in the middle of the room, reading a newspaper. He has his uniform on, including navy shorts. He glances up, notices me and then goes back to his paper. I walk towards him, slowly, since I'm frightened of slipping and falling on the polished floor. He glances again, and continues reading. I end up standing two feet away from him and ask,

'Are you waiting for me' He looks twice at me, literally!

'Wow, you look fantastic. I didn't recognise you!'

It was at this point I felt he became a little embarrassed at his wearing shorts. 'Please, sit down.' I do, again as always throughout this holiday, I am very aware of my poise, posture etc.

'Thank you' I give him my credit card and he asks me if everything is satisfactory. I tell him everything is fine and also (as instructed) that I am here alone and a bit nervous. He is very kind and we talk for a while. He is Yugoslav and has worked in London for some time before deciding to do some travelling and become a rep. He is older than most reps normally are, around thirty-ish. He is attractive, almost 'pretty,' with dark hair and seems pleasant.

As I stand to go to the restaurant he says, 'I eat here a couple of times a week, can I join you for dinner one evening?'

'Certainly,' I reply, 'be my guest.'

I go off to the restaurant (inside, I am skipping) feeling six feet tall. Not because he has asked to join me for dinner, but because I know that he was genuinely bowled over by the way I looked, and I knew then that I'd cracked it!

I feel I must give an explanation here. I know that appearances are deceptive, that's the whole point. I had achieved what I set out to do. He saw me and made a judgement about who I was and what I was about, before he had spoken to me. So, as it would transpire, did many of the other people in the hotel. Normally it doesn't matter, or does it? Whether we like it or not we all judge from appearances, it's nature. Hopefully, we then have the intelligence to know that beauty is not only in the eye of the beholder, but that appearance is only skin deep. It's what we are underneath that counts and I know that despite the fact that I like to wear nice clothes, I take them off. I don't take off my personality. This is always there and always the same. When it comes to it I don't need my make up or clothes to prove who I am, and never feel that I can't go out without my 'face on.' However, in the situation I have put myself in, and in order to have the confidence for me to take part, I felt that I have to look the part I wanted to play. That is, confidant, relaxed, poised, elegant, in control of my situation and as thought this is something very natural for me to be doing. In not wanting to stand out as being nervous, unsure, awkward and completely out of place, I have to do the opposite and stand out as something completely opposite. To be mouse like is not an option because that will make me vulnerable. By being opposite, I get their complete attention by making them feel slightly nervous and aware. _I_ don't have to show _my_ nerves. How ironic that I have knocked Michael out by appearing confident and composed, because I was too nervous to go as "myself". I hope you understand this, because this is fundamental to my holiday.

So, I appear at the restaurant. The impact is amazing. I am shown to my table on the terrace. It is much nicer out here. I have a window behind me and am shielded from those behind. There are two rows of tables. The weather is perfect as the moon shines a perfect reflection across the lake. It really does feel like being in a film. You could not create a more perfect picture. I feel much more relaxed and the waiters are lovely. They can't do enough for me and smile each time they pass my table. If this is what they are paid to do, full marks. Some of the people who are sitting near smile and say hello to me.

A couple sitting near me start to chat. As I sit waiting to for my food, I am aware of two men who are sitting at the table behind me. They were there when I came down to my table and I can tell that they are important guests. The waiters and the restaurant manager buzz around them like flies and I wonder who they are. After a time their food arrives. Not off the menu, although the menu is superb, they have delivered a huge lobster. It draws all eyes as it is paraded in front of them. Everyone is looking and even the man who has ordered it and whose face I can see as I turn round is impressed. I realise at this time that the other man is not quite the same, although I can only see his back. We all watch as one of the senior waiters extracts the flesh from the claws of this giant, and proceeds to carve it perfectly. Then slowly we all return to our own business. Just then someone taps me on the shoulder. It is the waiter who has been carving.

'The gentleman behind has asked if you would like to share their food.' All eyes are upon me.

I turn around and raise my glass, bow my head slightly and say 'Thank you.'

'We have more than enough.' He says. 'You are very welcome.'

The trolley containing the feast is wheeled to my table and the eyes follow, including those of my provider. Once again carving takes place and the plate is presented to me. It looks too beautiful to eat. The colours are out of a paint box, and I am rendered speechless. The trolley is withdrawn and the man raises his glass to me. I reciprocate and we all eat. I look at the couple that have spoken to me earlier. 'Enjoy,' he says as they smile at me. So I do.

I eat my bounty, delicious as it is, but almost as it hits my stomach I feel the scream of my digestive system as it objects to the complex plate of food that it is unaccustomed to. Later the two men rise to leave. The man whose face I could not see before turns round and smiles. I see now that he is a Downs syndrome man, but is older than is usual. I stand up and shake hands with both men and thank them again for their generosity. They are escorted from the restaurant and everyone relaxes. You could almost hear the sighs of relief. The restaurant manager comes to me and starts to tell me who they are.

He tells me that they are actually descendants from the Bleriot family. He says that the family came to this hotel every year until the mother died a few years ago. They are brothers and the man with Downs is around sixty years old. The other brother now lives in America and they come to the hotel every year on this day to stay usually for only one night to eat in the restaurant to celebrate the birthday of their dear departed mother. They rarely book, it is just expected they will be accommodated, and they always are. This year they had specified, as ever, exactly what they wanted to eat, and this lobster had had to be trawled and delivered from half way across Italy to satisfy their desire. Lucky lobster, I bet that made him feel better! I feel honoured that they shared their food with me and I also felt that I had passed some sort of test. No one knew me, and I had been chosen by this man to share his food. At that moment nobody knew how I was going to respond. Seemingly, I did so with grace and good manners and didn't let the side down. The side being the hotel staff who could control everything, but not this guest at the next table. She wasn't part of the plan and they all held their breath until it was all over.

At the end of my main course I am asked if I would like dessert. I am still uncomfortable having to go to the table and decline a sweet. Unperturbed, my waiter decides that I should have something and asks if I would like some sorbet.

'O.k.' I say.

'Lemon or strawberry?'

Damn, a decision!

'Or both?' He asks.

Phew, relief! 'Yes, both please.' And so begins a tradition during my stay. The sorbet is delicious and refreshing, and I have it almost every night.

As I finish my meal I am invited by the couple who had spoken to me earlier, to join them for coffee and a brandy at a bar just along from the hotel. I meet them in the glorious lounge, and off we go. We get on well immediately and laugh and joke about my rapid rise to fame. I confide that the food was rather rich and I may need to reach for the "Setlers" later!

They also give me a tip about crossing the road. Apparently, a man who arrived on the same day as me went out and was knocked down by a car whilst attempting to cross the road. He broke both legs and was whisked off to hospital. As if wrecking your holiday on the first day isn't bad enough, the police were going to prosecute him for not using the prescribed crossing!

We return to the hotel, and they go off to bed, I go into the piano bar for a drink and to think about my evening. I have my book as usual, but although it is open I don't read it. I just sit there thinking and waiting for my brandy. My brandy arrives, and I drink it slowly. I am now feeling quite at home and comfortable here, and at last start to relax.

VENICE

Next day is Monday and we are off to Venice. I meet my new friends at the bus stop opposite the hotel and we wait for the coach. They sit in front of me and we chat on the way. It is a long way, or so it seems and we are grateful for the air conditioning on the coach. We stop after a time at a service station, and are then given a lesson in how to buy coffee and food in an Italian service station. (Actually, it applies to many 'Café' type places here.) You order what you want, even coffee, then you pay for it. You are given a ticket/receipt and then move to another counter where you hand over your receipt and they then give you your food. Easy, But! It creates chaos to a coach load of tourists who want to do what we do here in good old Blighty! The tour guide intervenes, and like a good class of schoolchildren we all stand in line, take our turn and do as we are told. Then there are the toilets, where we have to cross the palm of the woman who stands guard at the door before we are allowed in. And she doesn't give change!

Refreshed, or more to the point, wrung out, we return to the coach for the next part of the journey and eventually arrive at the coach park outside Venice. We spot a temperature gauge on the side of a building. Forty-two degrees, bit warm even for me!

Our guide waves a telescopic radio aerial adorned with various glittery flowers and tells us to remember it. When we get to Venice there will be so many people she will hold it in the air and we must follow. We then board our water taxi. On the way she signs us up to various other commission bounty 'must dos.' The gondolas, the water ferry tour around some of the other islands, and the meal in the evening which she promises us is 'cheaper than eating in the hostelries we are likely to find unaided.' We are not so sure, but I decide that this might be easier than finding somewhere on my own, and actually she was right as my new friends found out before they joined us at the allotted hour having inspected various menus on their travels.

We arrive in Venice and it is unbearably hot. Our guide takes us along pointing out various sights and accompanying stories until we emerge into St Mark's Square. It really is lovely and almost empty, since it is so hot that it is impossible to stand in the middle for more than a couple of minutes. Even as I write this it is difficult to remember and imagine the heat. It's one of those 'had to be there' moments, but my friends will testify if you are in any doubt!

We are shown where the nearest toilets are and directed to the various places we may wish to explore, including the Grand Canal, and instructed what time to arrive back at the water taxi. Then we go.

I go off alone. My first port of call is to buy a parasol from one of the many street sellers we passed on the way to St. Mark's Square. I then walk off through the many narrow streets following my nose, looking in the various shops as I go. I eventually end up at the Grand Canal, and again it seems so familiar having seen it so many times on T.V, films and magazines. It is still wonderful to see it all in reality though.

I was asked by my travel agent friend to bring her back a baby's bib or something such like from Venice. She is pregnant and would love something from Venice. She offers to pay, but I have already decided to find something special for her as a gift for finding this so far wonderful holiday for me.

I am surprised that the cost of goods is not as high as I had expected. The designer shops have designer prices and are no different to anywhere else in the world, but the small shops here are, I consider, very affordable. I buy her a romper suit and some bootees. I then buy a couple of silk scarves for my friend and sister, and finally I buy two huge beautiful hand-decorated Venetian glass Christmas baubles, one for my friend and one for me. I expected that they would cost a fortune, but in fact they are really cheap. They are wrapped to within an inch of their life in bubble wrap, paper, and polystyrene bits and then boxed. If the plane goes down on the way home, bugger the black box, I'm with these!

I spend almost all of the day in these narrow streets, not least because it is too hot to go anywhere that the sun can penetrate. I drink loads of water. (No change there comes the cry from anyone who spends more than two minutes in my company!) It is impossible to go into The Basilica because it would involve queuing in the sun, and even with my parasol, the heat is too intense. Never mind, save that for another time.

At the allotted hour, I make my way back to our rendezvous and meet up with my new friends and we go first for the tour of the other islands, which if it was not so hot, would be really good, however we all sit melting inside the boat, too hot to be outdoors because of the sun. Glad to get off our impromptu sauna, we go to eat. Not fantastic, but more enjoyable than we had expected. Then off to our water taxi for the journey home. If the day has been torturously hot, the sight of Venice by night more than compensates for it. Truly romantic and glisteningly pretty I recommend this as one of the highlights. Dozing off on the way back I feel really happy.

THE DOLOMITES

Tuesday, and it's an early start for me. I'm off to the Dolomites. Camera at the ready and I board the coach looking forward to my day. There are not so many people on this excursion, and they are a really miserable bunch! Not that this bothers me, by now I am perfectly happy to be on my own. I am tired from the late return from Venice and doze along the way. The scenery changes to Swiss type chalets and it is hard to imagine we are still in Italy. We stop a few times on the way to take photographs and the journey is very easy. Of course, at the appropriate moment the guide comes along to ask us if we want to go to the top of the mountain on the cable car, all at discounted rates. She prepares us in advance by announcing it over the intercom and this gives me time to consider this proposition.

I have always had a fear of cable cars. I've never been on one, but I am frightened of it getting stuck and imagine being stranded there swinging gently in the breeze while someone is dropped from a helicopter to rescue me having first had to prise my knuckles from the rail inside and then persuade me over the course of a weekend to climb up a ladder onto the roof of my rocking cradle. Either that or the cable breaks and I plummet to earth in a belly flop that even I don't get up from. The third alternative to this nightmare is that the drive mechanism fails and I am party to one of the best white knuckle rides ever imagined as I zip slide towards the landing station whilst some kind tourist captures it all on video. I make the ten o'clock news in several languages but am not there to share my own moment of fame. Typical!

'Yes please.'

What? Did I just say that? Apparently so, as I have my ticket in my hand.

My cure for this nightmare I have is this. I have spent the last couple of weeks doing things I never thought I could do, not least coming on holiday on my own. If I can do this and enjoy it as much as I have, throwing off this cloak of self-doubt and gaining experiences that I would otherwise never have known, I can and must go up to the top of this mountain in a cable car.

We arrive and I follow the throng to the cable car. I hand over my ticket and get in. Nonchalantly, I walk to the window and lean against it. I have no fear! No, really, I have no fear. I must have left it on the coach, (and it was gone when I got back, maybe someone else picked it up?)

As the car moves away, I wonder how I will feel when I get to the top. Will I feel lonely? I like mountains, there is plenty of space to let your thoughts go free. Nothing to crowd them out and they don't get tangled up with the thoughts of everyone else like they do in confined spaces. But I wonder whether they will rattle around like a pea in the Grand Canyon. I will soon find out as the car slows to a stop and we all get off.

I find a quiet place some way away from everyone. It's not difficult as the mountaintop is extensive. I feel supremely calm and serene. If this is near heaven I'd like to book a place please. I never want to forget this moment. I have everything below me in my sights and nothing to be afraid of. I could have stayed here all day, in this one spot where I sat for a couple of hours motionless. The silence surrounding me as I left my physical being on the rock and floated around this beautiful place sung a haunting tune which I will never forget. I eventually tear myself away to take some photographs.

The journey back involves a couple more photo opportunities, and then we settle back. After a little while we all start to fiddle with the ventilation ducts above our seats. The air coming through it is hot. I call the guide and ask her if the coach driver can put the air conditioning back on. It's broken! Another two hours of melting and impromptu sauna. It is so hot I am surprised no one has fainted!

MICHAEL

I arrive back at the hotel 'glowing' as they politely term it, and see Michael in the lounge. He asks me if I enjoyed my trip to the Dolomites and I tell him it was wonderful apart from the journey back. He is full of apologies.

He asks me if he can join me for dinner tomorrow evening. 'Be my guest,' I reply, and am really pleased because there is something I want to ask him.

Wednesday. I wake early again, I find I am trembling. My whole body feels like a leaf on a tree as a gentle breeze tickles its underbelly. I think it is must be my nerves reminding me not to be too sure of myself.

I go down to the terrace where further along from the restaurant is the pool, and further than this is another, raised terrace, from which steps lead down to the lake. I find myself a sun bed and make myself comfortable doing absolutely nothing. Bliss! This is what it is all about.

Back in my room, my phone rings. It is the couple I met on the plane. Would I like to join them for lunch tomorrow? I can get the boat up to them and they will meet me at the landing stage. I am very touched that they think of me and although I feel nervous again at moving out of my own environment I agree to go.

I call Jane and then Christine. Tonight we decide I will wear my navy Escada dress. Very plain, fine wool seersucker with a split up the side. It is just above ankle length and understatedly elegant. I bought it from my friend who works in the shop where I buy most of my clothes. Pink and blue make up tonight and the gold sandals again. I also wear gold earrings and a gold necklace with an amber triangular coloured stone that spins on a spindle. It belonged to my mother and is just enough to set off the dress.

I meet Michael in the lounge at eight-thirty and we go to the restaurant. The waiters hastily set up another place for him and we share a glass of wine.

'So, how are you enjoying your stay?' He asks.

'Fantastic, I want to stay for another week!'

'Good. I'm glad you're enjoying yourself. You're o.k. on your own then?'

'Wonderful, I want to stay for another week.'

'Great!'

'Michael, I want to stay for another week.'

'I'm glad you have enjoyed yourself so much.'

'Michael, I mean it. I really want to stay for another week. Can you arrange it for me?'

'Really?'

'Really.'

'Oh, o.k. I'll see what I can do. I'm not sure if the hotel is full though, if it is I can arrange for you to stay at the Savoy.'

'No Michael, I want to stay here.'

'Let me see what I can do. I'll check tomorrow and leave you a message at reception.'

We continue our meal and I listen while Michael talks, and tells me all about himself, and Michael talks, and Michael tells me all about himself.... and Michael tells me all about himself! Actually that's not quite fair... but then again... yes it is...!

He is quite interesting, and I have exaggerated slightly, but I am sure if I had been a mirror he would have been just as happy. However, I have enjoyed his company, and he has certainly led an interesting life. I have a high regard for the way he left Yugoslavia, his homeland, and made a new life for himself during the time of conflict. I imagine you need, or perhaps develop a certain confidence or arrogance in order to succeed in such circumstances. Also, he is very professional at his job. (I later write to the travel company to tell them so.)

After our meal, we go for a drink at one of the local bars. He is a perfect gentleman, and he escorts me back to the hotel where I decide to go and have a brandy in the now familiar piano bar.

PIERO

Next thing, the young man who had delivered my brandy is standing in front of me. One arm behind his back, he bows deferentially towards me and asks very quietly, so that I find myself leaning forward to hear him,

'Excuse me madam, do you like champagne?'

I hear in my head 'Do you want sex?'

'Pardon?' comes out of my mouth.

'Do you like champagne' He repeats.

'Do you want sex?' I hear.

'What do you mean?' comes out of my mouth.

He looks slightly perplexed!

'I'm asking you, do you like champagne?'

'Yes.' I reply.

'Would you like to share some champagne with me later?'

'Do you want sex?' I hear.

'Just champagne?' comes out of my mouth.

Definitely looking confused he says, 'Just champagne, is it a difficult question, you are English aren't you?'

'Yes.' I reply. 'But why? Why do you want to drink champagne with me?' It's obvious I am a lot older than he is and I can't think of any reason why he would want to drink champagne with me.

'You have beautiful eyes,' he says.

'And you're Italian.' I say. Actually he has the most beautiful eyes I have ever seen. Piercing. A beautiful blue and eyelashes to die for. The whole effect is quite hypnotic.

'I mean it, you have beautiful eyes, and I would like to drink champagne with you. If you don't want to that's fine.'

'Thank you. That would be lovely.'

'I finish at eleven,' he says. 'I'll come to your room.'

'DO YOU WANT SEX?' I hear.

43

'No, you won't, I'll meet you by the pool.' I say.

'O.k.' he says.

What am I doing? I think to myself. Still I did stress, just champagne.

Eleven o'clock and I start to wander outside towards the pool. I walk slowly. It is another beautiful night. The moon is soft and warm, and casts a reassuring glow across the lake. I arrive at the pool and walk along. Out of nowhere he appears, gestures to be quiet, and leads me to the top terrace, which is obscured from the pool below by foliage. He sits me down on one of the sun beds and he sits on one next to it. Quietly he tells me that we are not allowed around the pool at night, I realise then why. It is right on the edge of the lake and they need to make sure none of the residents end up in the lake after a few too many, never to be seen again. It would be bad for business! Also all the rooms are on this side of the hotel and late night revellers would cause too much noise for those wishing to slumber. At that moment he grabs my arm and drags me to shadows of the foliage. Pointing at a man who is walking along the edge of the pool, he whispers that he is the night watchman. We wait with baited breath and after a few minutes the man goes away. Whilst we are waiting I think to myself, I can't believe I'm hiding in the bushes in my posh dress, in a hotel where I'm paying to stay!

'Should we go?' I ask

'No, we are o.k. He has done his rounds now and will not be back. He goes round twice, and he had already been once before you arrived. As long as we're quiet we'll be o.k.'

We go back to our seats. He opens the champagne deftly. I have seen him working in the bar and he certainly seems to have a way about him that is different to the other bar staff. Much more expert and flowing in his work than the others I have seen. A master of his art!

We chink our glasses as we start to sip the cold champagne, and then we start to talk. He tells me he is a wine taster, or is training to be one. It takes several years to qualify and he has only one year left. He shows me his wine tasters identity card, (just in case I don't believe him!) He also tells me that the staff are not allowed to mix with the guests, if they do they are sacked. As we talk and I start to relax a little, I understand why he suggested my room! As the time passes I really start to like him. The setting is perfect and whilst in the films he takes her in his arms and kisses her passionately, and then they disappear into the sunset to live happily ever after, I am sitting here happily, with a lovely young man, drinking champagne, in a beautiful country, dressed up to the nines, being pampered and without a care in the world. What more could a girl want.

After a while I ask him why he invited me to drink champagne with him. He says again 'because you have beautiful eyes.'

'Come off it, you have got eyes to die for, mine are nothing like that.'

'You have beautiful blue eyes,' he says 'and they are captivating. There is something very unusual about them, and I wanted to get to know you better because of them.'

Hmm. Not sure about this but I'll go along with it for now.

Eventually, he asks me, 'Can I kiss you please?'

Typical, he just wants sex!

'Look I don't want sex with you. I told you, just champagne.' and I meant it.

'I know. I just wanted to kiss you, I don't want sex with you.'

'Why!' I say outraged, but laughing.

He laughs as well and says. 'I just want to kiss you.'

I feel embarrassed at this, but say 'o.k.'

He kisses me lightly on the lips. 'Can I kiss you again?'

'No!'

We talk for quite a long time and eventually he leans over to me and kisses me again. This time I find myself kissing him back. I have had a bit to drink tonight, but not enough to lose my senses. However there is something about this young man that I like, let alone his beautiful eyes and nice body. I decide to give in with the knowledge that tomorrow morning he may ignore me and I become another conquest. What the hell, I'm here to enjoy myself and right now, I'm really enjoying myself. Not that I sleep around, I don't and this is something so out of character for me. I tell him, 'look I don't sleep around and I don't know you.'

'And I don't know you.' he replies.

True, I think, he doesn't!

Somehow we end up under the bushes, it's great, strangely romantic, despite the bushes and I have no regrets, although as I dust down the sand from my dress, I have a mental image in my mind, hair and glasses askew, lipstick smudged, dress slightly creased!

As we straighten ourselves up, he tells me he will have to go and break in to get us back into the hotel.

'Why?' I ask.

'Because we're not allowed to mix with the guests, and at night they lock all the doors. The only way in is through the front. You can go in that way, but if we go in, in quick succession, someone will notice. Wait here, I'll be back for you.'

He goes off and for a moment I wonder if he will come back or not. After what seems like ages, and he still has not returned, I really do wonder. Then he reappears.

'Go to the door at the back of the bar, I'll come and let you in.'

I go as quietly and as quickly as my shoes and the shale will allow, to our rendezvous. As I head towards the door, he flies down to me, sweeps me off my feet into his arms, and carries me inside. Wow, now this really is like the old movies!

I find myself in the kitchen behind the bar. He locks the doors and we are alone again, in relative safety.

'Coffee?' he asks.

'Yes, please.'

I watch as he makes us both coffee. We drink and talk some more, and eventually he takes me down some stairs, along corridors and eventually emerge through a door where he kisses me goodnight and disappears. I look round at the door after it closes. It has a huge mirror attached to it, and once closed you would never guess it is a door. I feel a bit like Alice spat out from a rabbit hole staring back through the looking glass. Very surreal! I go to my room and climb into bed. I sleep soundly and happily.

Next morning, (Thursday) I wake and think to myself, ooh, this is the bit where you feel, 'Shit, what have I done!' or 'Bloody hell that was a great night!' Which is it to be?

'Bloody hell that was a great night!'

Then I remember that I am going to meet the couple off the plane. I get up and find, not for the first time this holiday, I am trembling. I thought that it was just nerves and still am not sure, but today, I seem to be shaking more than ever, and I have a supreme headache. Basically I feel like shit! All I really want to do is go down to the terrace and relax, but I have to get on the ferry and go to meet the people off the plane. I go to breakfast and hope that once I've had something to eat I will feel better. I drink lots of water, and have some coffee. Then I go to the ferry.

Big mistake!

As I get on the heat hits me. The temperature outside is around thirty-two degrees, and this is o.k. but the heat inside the ferry is almost unbearable. I meet the couple that were on the transfer bus with me and chat to her until they get off at one of the stops along the lake. She asks me how I am getting on and I tell her I am having a great time apart from today when I feel ill.

Maybe the combination of all that rich food, alcohol, nerves, late night (and fun) mixed in with the heat has just got a bit too much for me. They get off and I continue my journey, all the time thinking, 'Why am I doing this, I don't have to do anything I don't want to.' Of course it is because I am so grateful for the care that this couple showed to me and they are looking forward to me coming. We are to have lunch and I will get the last ferry back in time for dinner this evening. However, the longer I am on the ferry the worse I feel and by the time I arrive I have broken out into a sweat which has nothing to do with the heat.

They are there waiting and smiling. They make a huge fuss of me and take me off for a coffee. Grateful to sit down in the fresh air I try to convince myself I am feeling better. No such luck! Another coffee and they ask me all about how I am getting on. I tell them about the dinner last night, and how I am really enjoying myself. They are not so keen, their hotel is full of mainly German people, and they feel they do not fit in. Also their hotel is at the top of a steep hill and although there is a courtesy bus available at the drop of a hat to ferry them up and down to the town, they feel rather trapped.

I realise as they are talking that there is no way I am going to last the day. Why I don't tell them that I feel ill I don't know. I know they will be disappointed and probably make a fuss about my health, but all I really want to do is go back to the hotel where I now feel happy, secure and comfortable. So, how do I get out of this? Just then they ask me what time I have to leave. I check the timetable and see a ferry is leaving at three fifteen.

'Three fifteen.' I say.

'Oh, so early. We thought you could stay all day.'

'Well by the time the ferry gets back and I get ready for dinner, I really need to leave around three.' Not a lie really, because feeling like I do I know I need to go and lie down for a couple of hours before I go to dinner.

'We'd better go to eat then.' He says smiling.

'Yes' she says. 'I'm really disappointed that you have to leave so early, I wanted to go shopping with you.'

I feel guilty, but know that I am more likely to faint or throw up over her than go shopping! We go to their hotel via their hotel courtesy bus. We find a table on the terrace outside the restaurant and the menu arrives. The sight of it brings beads of sweat to my brow. They are talking three-course meal here, 'You must be joking!' I think to myself. Even if I was on top form I couldn't eat a three-course meal at lunchtime and another in the evening.

'To be honest, I don't eat that much at lunch time.' Another look of disappointment crosses her face. 'I find it too hot to eat and tend to eat my main meal at night' I wait for the response.

'You're right.' He says. She is going to take a bit more convincing.

'If I eat too much for lunch I find I am not hungry at night.' I wait again.

'I never thought of that.' She says. 'No wonder we never feel like eating all that food at night, perhaps we are eating too much in the day.'

Relief! I think I have won this battle, although the effort has made me feel intensely wobbly. Keen to capitalise on my advantage, I decide. 'I'm going to have a cheese and ham toastie.'

She looks horrified, did I say 'cheese and ham toastie' or did 'shit sandwich' fall out of my mouth!

Another discussion takes place as I metaphorically pick her up off the floor.

'Cheese and ham toastie?' she says. 'You can't have that, you must have something proper.'

'Let her have what she wants.' he says.

'But she can't just have that, can she.' We then proceed to go through the whole menu whilst she tries to persuade me to have something 'proper' to eat.

Twenty minutes later…

'...So that's three cheese and ham toasties please.' He says to the waitress.

'Are you sure you don't want something else? Maybe a salad to go with it?' she's still persisting even as we wait. Her face shows the look of a child brought up on McDonalds who has just been given a plate of vegetables. Total disdain!

Eventually the toasties arrive, He looks pleased. She is still unsure. We start to tuck in. Her husband and I wait for the verdict.

'These are really nice.' She announces.

I struggle through my food but am relieved my perseverance paid off. Conscious of the time I am worried that I will be late for the ferry. We have more coffee and I go to the loo. I wash my face and gather myself for the next bout.

'Gosh, I don't know where the time has gone.' I say hinting and hoping they look at their watch.

'What time do you have to go again?' he asks.

'The ferry leaves at three fifteen.'

'I wish you could stay,' she says 'I was really looking forward to showing you round the shops.'

'Yes, never mind, we've had a nice lunch haven't we, and it is really kind of you both to have invited me.'

'Yes, and you're right about eating too much at lunch time, that was just enough. I bet we'll really enjoy our dinner.'

The bus is summoned and we are dropped off at the bottom of the hill. We walk through the small town and she shows me a few treasures she has found. I 'Ooh' and 'Ahh' at the right time and then head off for the ferry. Gratefully for me we arrive early.

'Time for a coffee' he declares.

'Lovely' I lie. I think I will drown in the stuff if I have any more, but know it is easier to drink this than not.

Then I am at the landing stage and am really happy to see the ferry arrive. With a hug and a kiss, the exchange of addresses and a promise to keep in touch, I walk up the gangway to safety. We wave to each other as the ferry moves off and I find a place outdoors for the journey back. Disaster definitely papered over, but the paper is only tissue thick and whilst the exact truth is obscured from their sight, I know they could still smell a rat.

So, why didn't I just come clean and tell them I didn't feel well? No idea!

All the way back I feel ill. I feel like my legs are going to give way under me but if I go inside where I can sit down I think I will faint or throw up. So, I stand all the way back and as the hotel comes into sight I start to feel relieved. Once back safely I go to my room and lie down on the bed. I sleep for about two and a half hours and feel much better when I wake.

Telephone call to Christine. I tell her about the day and she agrees that it was right and proper to go, in spite of how I was feeling. I tell her about last night and she thinks it's great. So what does tonight have in store, we wonder? And more importantly, what to wear!

Tonight it is a pair of ivory trousers with ivory camisole and ivory devore over-shirt and of course the gold sandals, accessorised with jewellery and a matching clutch bag.

I go down to the restaurant, and am greeted as ever with smiles and attentiveness. The couple I went for a drink with chat to me and the other guests look at me. I think maybe it is because of what I wore for the meal last night. I also notice that more of the ladies seem to be dressed up. Have they seen me and decided if she can do it so can I? Have they all brought their posh frocks, just in case, and now feel confident enough to wear them?

I drink only a little wine with my meal and stick with my friend, water. At the end, my new friends invite me for coffee and brandy again, and after my sorbet, I go with them.

I tell them about my disastrous day and it seems really funny when retold. They tell me not to worry and to enjoy the rest of my stay. They go to their room and I go to the piano bar.

In the bar, the bar manager comes over to me. 'Hi, how are you?'

'Fine thanks. You?'

'Yes. What would you like to drink?'

'Hmm, I'm not sure, I've been wobbly all day. Perhaps I should stick to brandy.'

'Wobbly eh? It's probably the brandy, it affects your blood pressure, you know. Take my advice, stop drinking brandy while you are here, it's too hot.'

'Oh! O.k. Thank you.'

'Do you like champagne?'

Deja vous! 'Yes.'

'O.k., this is the best, pink champagne, Winston Churchill's favourite!' He pours me a glass with all necessary decoration and I drink.

'Delicious, thank you.'

'I hear you caused a bit of a storm in the restaurant the other night?'

'Yes, it was lovely. Nice to be spoilt now and again.'

'So what is this you are reading?' He takes my book and I start to laugh.

'Have you heard of it?'

'No, what's it about?' he walks off with it and starts to read. He laughs at some of the extracts he picks on.

'Me! Or at least I feel a bit like her anyway.'

We start to talk and he tells me he thinks I look German. 'So what are you doing here and on your own?'

I explain briefly.

'And do you like it?

'Love it, it's the best thing I've ever done.' I reply.

'Hmm, you're interesting, it's your eyes, they're unusual, you make me nervous.'

'And you're Italian!'

'No really, you make me nervous.'

'Get lost, I'm not that daft.'

'Do you like the hotel?'

'It's beautiful, very colonial.'

'Well of course, it is, Churchill used to come here.'

'I know and I understand why. It's like stepping back to the nineteen twenties; I can hear all the laughter and see all the people here enjoying themselves. I can just see this woman wearing a Charleston dress with fringes, tossing her hair back and laughing as she swings her pearls and smokes her cigarette from a long cigarette holder.'

'Are you psychic?'

'What?'

'Are you psychic? Can you really see her?'

The question of 'being psychic' is a big subject. For the moment I will just say this. I don't know if I am psychic or not. Firstly because I do not think I am the right person to judge. Some people say I am, I really don't know. Maybe it's just having a wild and vivid imagination, maybe it's intuition or perhaps it's life experience. It could be any or all of these things, or something else, or none. Who knows? But in order for anyone to say or think that you are, you have to speak and have the confidence to say things that may sound completely loopy, and then run the risk of being ridiculed and thought of as weird, (No problem there then!) and I explain this to him.

'I don't know' I reply. 'I just know that ever since I have been here I have 'seen' this woman everywhere, but I hadn't really thought about it until now.'

'What. Like a ghost?'

'No, I don't see ghosts, I have feelings, and images in my mind's eye, and sometimes they are difficult to differentiate from my imagination.'

'What's she like?'

'Happy and carefree, she wears a black dress with white polka dots.'

'Anything else?'

'She's got short blonde hair, thick and it has a natural wave.'

'I'm scared.'

'Why? There's nothing to be scared of. It's the live ones you need to watch out for!'

We chat some more and I go off to bed.

Friday. I am glad to have nothing planned. I check with reception to see if Michael has managed to sort out my staying for another week. (I have already called work to see if I could have another week off. "Of course. We expected you to." I am told. This is a big surprise to me. Seems they know more about me than I do!) He has left a message to call him. I find he has arranged to change my flight and I can stay for another week. 'But' he says, 'I will have to move into another hotel for three nights.' It's a first class four-star modern hotel and only two hundred metres away. Thanking him, I accept, but ask him to keep trying for a room in this hotel. He says he will and will be in touch. I take my book and sunglasses and find a sun bed under one of the gazebo tents. In between reading, and dozing, I digest my surroundings.

Around lunchtime, the people start to move away as they go to eat. Although it never feels crowded, I still feel happier when there are fewer people about, and it is quieter. I decide to go swimming in the lake. Another small hurdle to jump since I have to walk down to some concrete steps to the landing stage. I stand up, making sure my bikini is covering all the right bits, pull my stomach in, stand tall and walk as elegantly as is possible on the searingly hot sand and concrete. I find myself at the edge of the steps where the water gently caresses my feet cooling them down again. This place on the steps becomes somewhere I like to stay very much. The water with its regular rhythm kisses the beautiful moss that clings to the stonework. The greenest of green, this moss really does feel like a carpet of velvet under my feet, and I remember a few days back, to that morning at breakfast when I first studied the water and felt then its velvety softness without having touched it. I sit for a while to get used to the temperature of the water, and as I do I become almost hypnotised by the moss. When the water is away it hangs heavily against its host, then the water returns and the moss dances elegantly and in perfect time to the rhythm of this waters music. It never loses time or enthusiasm. Sometimes, when the water is away I run my hand across the moss and squeeze all its moisture from within. The colour change is dramatic. Its oxygen asphyxiated for a few moments, it is paralysed and unable to move. Almost choking for the return of its life source it turns a pale insipid shade of its former self, its texture changing to something resembling coconut matting. I think I must remember this event to record somewhere so moved am I by its beauty. Many months later, I tell my friend Mario of this story and ask the Italian name for moss. He tells me 'muschio,' how appropriate, I think, this word is so close to the word 'musico,' Italian for music.

Once able to detach myself from this delight, I stand as I prepare to make my entrance to the lake. I haven't dived for many years, and hope I don't make a complete fool of myself. In I go, head first as ever, and resurface unscathed. The water really is so beautifully silky soft against my skin, and having had time to warm itself during the summer months, it is possible to stay in here for a long time. I swim out to one of the three buoys anchored a short distance away and float around taking in the scenery from this new perspective and as boats pass by I bob around like a cork. I can see the hotel as it is meant to be seen, rising up out of the lake. It is not possible to see it properly on land since it sits so close to the water's edge and you can't get it all in your field of vision. Eventually, I swim back to the shore and return to my sun bed. Cooled by the refreshment of the lake and tired from swimming, I soon go to sleep. I am woken to the sound of a voice and, opening my eyes against the sun, a man is standing next to me, tray in hand.

'Cocktail for the lady.' It is Piero; He stands above me greeting me with a smile, and a beautiful pink-frosted glass. 'You ordered a melon cocktail?'

'Thank you.' In fact I haven't ordered anything, but take this gift with great delight. I am slowly aware that everyone around me is looking towards me, again! The couple with whom I have been sharing brandy with in the evenings are seated nearby. We exchange glances and smile. Piero asks me quietly if I would like to go to eat with him in the evening. I say yes, and we agree to meet in the car park across the road at seven-thirty.

Arriving back at my room some time later, the old problem is back. What to wear. The answer is also the same as usual, call Christine! We decide on my knee length navy shift dress. Make up pink and blue, lower heeled shoes (in case I have to walk!) and matching bag.

Not wanting to appear too eager, I leave my room at seven-thirty and after pausing at the restaurant to say I won't be eating tonight, make my way across to the car park. Because the hotel is so long, it takes me ten minutes to get there. I wonder whether he will be there already, if at all, and am relieved to find him sitting on a bench waiting for me. A kiss on either cheek and we walk towards the many cars parked below.

I look to see which one I think will belong to Piero. As we get nearer I see three cars. One silver sports car, and two older more 'ordinary' cars, both black and I decide the older looking of these two will be my carriage for the evening. Piero walks alongside one of them and I head towards the passenger side. Forgetting that the driver's side is on the left, I suddenly realise I am standing at the wrong car. He is opening the passenger door of the silver sports car for me to get into!

'Is this yours?' I ask.

'Yes.'

'It's beautiful.'

'Thank you. I like good food and wine, and nice cars. People ask me how I can afford all this. I work hard and spend my money how I like. My manager is, I think, a little jealous that I can afford this at my age. If he knew I was out with you he would definitely sack me.'

I am whisked off to a Tuscan restaurant half way up a mountain and again feel like a twelve-year old child. Awkward and out of my depth. We are shown to a table and handed a menu. 'Arrgghh' what to order!

'Aperitif?'

'Yes please.' He speaks to the waitress, and as we drink, we study the menu.

'What would you like?' he asks.

'Please, you order for me.' I respond, inspirationally. (Please let it not be the seafood in the bucket, I pray.)

'O.k.' The waitress reappears and obviously knows him. They talk a little and then she goes. Reappearing with a bottle of red wine, He swirls the contents she has poured into the bowl of the large glass. Taking a deep breath of its perfume, he announces 'a little young but o.k.' Tasting, then, the dizzy liquid, he nods acceptance, and she pours two glasses. As I lift my glass by the bowl, he reminds me to hold it by the stem. Oops! Faux pas.

Next thing our starter arrives. Oh no, it's the bucket of seafood!

'I hope you like seafood.' He says.

'Love it.' I lie. (Please let me not throw up when this hits my mouth!) I watch him start, (since I am not sure of the etiquette required to eat this,) before I take my first shell. Removing the contents I deposit it in my mouth and wait for my body's reaction. 'Mmm, this is beautiful,' I hear myself saying, and I mean it. This is really delicious and at this moment I am cured of my phobia for eating shellfish out of a bucket, (although shellfish from the seaside, "in the raw" will take some hypnosis and a feeding tube to conquer.)

Next arrives steak. Cooked to perfection. Then dessert and of course a dessert wine to accompany it. Coffee and brandy, and I am extremely full, 'slightly' drunk but by now, comfortable, I no longer feel like a twelve-year old.

Saturday, and I check with reception for any message from Michael. Yes. Instructions to check into the other hotel for three nights and then return here for the rest of the duration. Happy to be staying, but I am disappointed to move. This hotel is one of the main reasons I want to stay. I ask the receptionist.

'I really want to stay here. Are you sure you don't have a room?'

She checks. 'No sorry.'

'Not even a twin room?'

She checks. 'No, sorry.'

'A suite?'

She checks. 'Yes, we do have a suite for these three days. Would you like to upgrade?'

'Yes please.' Yahee! Looks like I can stay.

'O.k., do you want to move room or do you want to stay where you are?'

'Stay where I am please. I don't mind paying the extra, but I like the room I am in.'

'O.k. No problem.' I try to avoid running, but rush back to my room to call Christine and Jane. I also call Michael, and tell him the news. He is pleased, but I think a bit miffed that I arranged a room that he had been unable to secure.

'I need to see you to arrange to pay for the cost of changing the flight. It is forty pounds.' Michael says.

'O.k. let me know when you will be in the hotel and thanks very much for your help'

'You're welcome.'

In the evening I change for dinner. A long black crepe dress, split up one side, with gold trim, bought in one of the local shops. Fits like a glove.

Arriving in the restaurant I am escorted to my seat by one of the waiters. At the table next to me is an old man with a younger female. He acknowledges my presence by standing slightly. I find out he is French, and of course any French I know leaves my head in an instant. During the rest of my stay, we perform a ritual at mealtimes.

Breakfast: He is the only guest to have a table reserved, and it is the table I have for dinner. The reason he changes tables for breakfast is that the sun is in the wrong place for him to sit at his usual table, causing him discomfort.

I trawl my brain for some French language and we say good morning, how are you, talk about the weather, we speak about the lake and what we are doing today. He asks me "am I eating lunch?" I say "no." He is always surprised at this, and then we depart to enjoy our respective day.

The conversation about the lake is always interesting in spite of the language barrier. The lake seems to breathe a life of its own and rises and falls each day depending on its mood. Always passive, but the slight change in air pressure is, to me, very apparent when I look at the water. I tell this man what I think the day will be like compared to the day before and he is always interested.

Evenings: He always greets me with a smile and small bow, tells me I look beautiful, and I thank him. We talk about the day, what we have done in simple language (or with a bit of help from the waiter) and then eat.

Afterwards I go to the piano bar. My new friends have gone home today and we exchange addresses before they leave. They make me promise to phone when I get back and tell them the rest of my adventure here, and invite me to stay with them in the near future.

I talk to the bar manager as is now customary and Piero quietly delivers me another cocktail he has created.

One evening, whilst sitting reading my book, the bar manager comes to me.

'Will you stop reading that book!'

'Why?'

'Every night you sit here reading. Tonight you sit without your book!' I'm not sure why he says this, but he takes my book off me and puts it behind the bar. At the time it seems reasonable!

Within ten minutes a man sitting at the bar offers me a drink. Not champagne this time, but port. I decline politely, but next thing I am delivered a glass of port. He comes over to me, and says it is just a courteous gesture. He looks around mid-sixties, craggy faced and I realise he is German. For the next half hour this man tells me how much he hates the British. A complete fascist, he is one of the rudest people I have ever met, and clearly a bit of a drunkard. Eventually I've had enough. I tell him what a completely rude man he is and ask him to go away.

He then asks me if I would like to go out with him on the lake in his beautiful boat.

'What a cheek.' I reply. 'After the way you have just spoken to me I wouldn't go out of the door with you. As for going on the lake in a boat with you, you must be joking. I'd probably end up at the bottom of the lake with a lump of concrete tied to my ankles!'

He takes the hint and leaves. I complain to the bar manager about how rude he has been and ask him why he didn't rescue me.

'You didn't need any help, you seem to know exactly how to handle him!' He replies.

So, it seems I am developing a new language here;

Champagne = Sex

Cocktails = Discrete attention

Port = Verbal abuse!

Sunday. I relax by the lake again, go swimming, read my book and look forward to another week here. The evening arrives quickly and I go to eat. I find another English couple have replaced my friends at their table, and we soon start talking. They arrived yesterday and today have been out and about walking. They tell me I am welcome to join them anytime I like.

In the piano bar I find the other rep and she joins me for a drink. She has heard I am staying for another week and is keen to talk to me. I tell her I am very grateful to Michael for arranging things for me, especially as I know he did all of this on his day off. He has also not charged me any commission on the cost of changing my flight. I realise that these two don't get on particularly well, but she agrees he is conscientious and good at his job. She is surprised to find I am drinking a champagne cocktail courtesy of the bar manager. Not a regular gift she tells me.

Monday, and at breakfast, the couple I spoke to last night invite me to accompany them for a walk. I decide to go, and we walk to a nearby town, larger than this one and livelier. The shops are beautiful and I spy an Escada shop. I make a mental note to return. We talk all the way there exchanging stories and again we seem to hit it off really well.

Over the course of the next week we often walk together in the mornings after breakfast, before going our separate ways for the rest of the day. They also join me in the bar for a drink on a couple of occasions.

The rest of this second week falls into a bit of a pattern. It is very relaxing and I spend a lot of time swimming in the lake. Sometimes the lifeguard who is also the pool attendant, talks to me, He is always flirting with any potential females and I am always laughing when he fails. One day in the lake, floating on one of the buoys we talk for a long time as he tells me about himself and the difficult life he left behind in his motherland. I cannot remember where he originated from, but I know it was one of the Latin-America's.

In the afternoon I am lying under the gazebo, dozing, and become aware that people are moving away. I am face down and really comfortable, so take no real notice. After a time I realise something is wrong. Raising my head, I can see the storm clouds approaching. Completely unworried, I take no notice as everyone moves away. I am sure it is just a shower and under the gazebo, I have nothing to fear.

Wrong!

The sun terrace, outside bar, pool and landing stage are all deserted as the first dinner-plate size drops of rain fling themselves down. I realise it's time to go. There are only a couple with a teenage girl and me left. Suddenly, the pool attendant appears with the mattress off a sun bed offering protection for us back to the hotel. He takes the others first and then comes back for me. By now the weather is having a seriously good time at my expense. Ice cubes are falling from the sky. Yes, I do mean ice cubes. I am now soaking wet, and because of this I am unable to fasten my bikini top. In my hour of need the pool attendant fastens it for me and we eventually arrive indoors, very wet with a large audience to welcome our arrival. I can imagine what they are thinking. "English, I suppose. Serves you right for not following our example!"

Within twenty minutes the storm is over. I go to my room to dry off and as I do, I look out to the front of the hotel. The road below is flooded by around three feet of water with cars submerged up to their bonnets. I am amazed that in such a short time so much water could fall from the sky. Within another twenty minutes, the sun is back, everywhere is dry, and only the photographs I have taken prove it has happened. Back on the terrace the pool attendant comes to see if I am all right. I tell him he has gone up in my estimation, since this must be one of the only times in his life he has a woman's bikini in his grasp, and he fastens it up thereby relinquishing an opportunity!

He agrees!

In the evening, having found my way back to the Escada shop and bought a few more goodies for my wardrobe, (essential of course since I only packed for one week) I change for dinner. I never wear the same outfit more than twice.

THE FRENCH MAN

I learn from the restaurant manager more about my French friend. He is a very eminent French judge. He comes to the hotel a couple of times a year for around three weeks each time. He has been doing so for many years. The lady who is with him is his companion/personal assistant and she looks after his every need. I ask what he does every day since I see him around reception and in the office there. He tells me he is still working and he receives Fax's and messages. He deals now mainly with refugees and human rights, and has been bestowed with the highest honour that France can bestow on any man in his position.

I realise now why he commands such attention. Very quiet but expects to be treated properly. Every evening, he spends at least twenty minutes discussing the options for the menu before deciding. Invariably he has almost the same. Melon in port to start, Steak for main course, but has a different sweet made especially for him. The most amusing part of this discussion I overhear each night revolves around potatoes. They discuss every combination of cooked potatoes before he always decides, mashed!

The restaurant manager has infinite patience with this man but admits to me that sometimes he does become a little tired of the same conversation, which does not alter from one trip to the next. But he tells me this man is extremely clever and is consulted over many judgemental issues in France. He is a rare and unique individual and deserves every attention.

I am happy to have not known this for the first couple of days I have seen him, and been allowed to form my opinion of him as any other person, and without the risk of any influence of his status. By the end of my holiday we have struck a real affection for one another.

Every night his specially prepared dessert is served to him, and within two days of his arrival, after he has been served his portion, he sends it to me and I take a portion, whatever is left is then delivered to the big table. It is always sumptuous, and often contains lots of cream and chocolate. But I still have my sorbet either before or after, and towards the end of my stay the restaurant manager tells me they will rename the sorbet in my honour!

THE BAR MANAGER

Several times, as I pass through the bar during the day on my way back from a walk, I see the bar manager. He plays golf and I ask how his round has gone. Every time he says "Terrible, and I blame you for putting me off my swing." I always laugh and continue on my way. In the evenings he always spends a long time talking to me and says he thinks I am a witch. He always wants to know what I can see. Are there any ghosts lurking and is the woman I described still around. He tells me he has been scared since a party of 'psychics' came to the hotel and one of them told him the hotel had a lot of bad vibes, especially at the very far end of the hotel.

It transpires that the hotel had been taken over by the Germans as a hospital during the Second World War, and the farthest end of the hotel was the mortuary. I start to laugh.

'No wonder she said that. It's easy to say this is a bad place when you know it was full of dead bodies! Don't worry about it. Take it from me there is nothing bad in this place. Ask any of the guests. If they felt bad about it they would soon let you know.'

'Will you go and see though?'

'What do you mean?' I ask.

'Will you go and look for me and tell me if there are any bad things there.'

'If you like.'

'Now?'

'O.k.'

'And you will tell me if you find anything bad won't you?'

'Yes, o.k.'

'Promise?'

'Promise.'

I go to walk to the far end of the hotel. It is very late and the hotel is very long. Around one third of a mile from one end to the other I am told.

I have to admit that it is a bit scary walking along especially now I know there used to be a mortuary here. But then I think to myself, what would I think and feel if he had not told me this? I think I wouldn't be scared. I stop and look ahead.

The corridor comes to an end and there is a doorway on the far left of the corridor that leads to the rooms that were once the mortuary. I pause to consider. There is no light in this doorway and because of where it is you can't see beyond. At this precise moment, the light sensor is triggered and a young couple emerge laughing and happy. We exchange greetings and I return to the bar.

'Well?' He asks.

'No problem.' I reply.

'Sure?'

'Stake your life on it.'

'You would tell me, wouldn't you?'

'Promise.'

'How do you know?'

'Because the light came on, and a couple came out laughing and happy. It has a lovely atmosphere.'

'I believe you.' He says. 'So what can you tell me about me then?'

I look at him and see a grey aura around him. 'Do you really want me to tell you?'

'Yes, is it bad?'

'No, but I can see a big man around you. He has grey hair, receding, and I think he comes to you when you are tired.'

'Is he here now?'

'Yes.' He starts moving around and tells me he is scared. 'There's nothing to be scared of. But I don't want to frighten you. I won't say anymore if you are worried.'

'No, I want to know, tell me some more.'

'Look, I don't know if what I see or feel is right or not, but I will tell you what I think and you must judge for yourself.'

'O.k.'

'I think this man looks after you when you get really tired. I think there are times when you are near exhaustion, not just the usual sort of tiredness we all get, but thoroughly exhausted. There are times when you feel you are almost ready to collapse and these are the times this man is close to you. This bar is very important to him, and so are you.'

'Who is he?'

'I don't know.'

'Is he related to me?'

'No, I don't think so.'

'What does he look like?'

'He is bigger than you, strong, kind and the bar is really important to him. He puts his arms under your armpits and keeps you from falling over. He is around late fifties early sixties, and his time was many years ago.'

He goes on to tell me that when the Germans took over the hotel, the bar manager at the time refused to give up the bar. Despite many threats from the Germans, he kept the bar open all throughout the occupation.

I ask him about his own health and ask him if I am right about his tiredness sometimes. He tells me that a few years ago he was involved in a serious car accident and despite being almost fully recovered, he still has some problems and fatigue is one of them. He tells me the reason he plays golf every day is to keep fit and he has become a bit of a hypochondriac.

I find out later about the accident in which he was involved. Everyone at the scene thought he was dead. He was taken to hospital and was not expected to survive. He was then told he would never walk again. Every day for three years he went swimming, walking, playing golf, running. Every single day, unrelenting, including Christmas, he worked himself to get fit again. He adopted a healthy diet and lifestyle and apart from a very slight limp, few would ever guess what had happened. As I got to know him a little better, he also told me the story. I really came to admire his stoicism and commitment to recover and get back to normal, and I felt he had every right to indulge in a little of the vanity I saw in him. He had supreme courage and the wisdom to know that he was the only one who could help himself to get better. I drink a toast to him!

Waking to the start of another typical day I go to breakfast. I exchange pleasantries with the judge and then go for a walk with my friends. We talk all the time and it feels like we have known each other for years. We walk to a place further along the lake and go swimming. Then we see storm clouds starting to gather, and mindful of the last episode, return to the shelter of a café before returning to the hotel.

As we reach the hotel reception, the lady of the couple I am with goes to the toilet, leaving me standing talking to her partner. We are laughing over another of the many jokes he tells me. Out of the blue, Michael appears.

'I need to talk to you.' He says, quite demandingly.

'Oh, right.' I walk away towards him and he asks me, could I let him have the money for the flight.

'Yes, of course. Would you like it now?'

'No, tonight will be fine, if that is convenient for you.'

'Certainly. Would you like to join me for dinner?'

'Yes please. That would be lovely. Around eight o'clock in the bar?'

'Fine. See you then.'

I return to my friends and he is really laughing. 'He thought I was chatting you up, you know. He was jealous!' Laughing, we go our separate ways.

A couple of small showers and the sun returns. I take my place under the gazebo and relax the afternoon away sleeping and reading.

Seven-thirty. The weather is threatening. Extremely humid and still around thirty-two degrees. I wear a new Escada suit I bought a few days ago. Hipster trousers, halter neck top and loose fitting jacket with matching sling-back shoes. All in lightweight grey wool, trimmed in black. Altered to fit overnight and delivered to my room. Very chic and I feel like the bees knees.

I leave the hotel to go across the road to the cash point machine. As I walk out a voice calls me. Piero, he is leaning out of a window. 'Don't go far, it's going to rain.'

'Don't worry I'm just going to the cash point. See you in the bar in five minutes.' I get back just in time.

Once in the bar, Piero asks, 'Aperitif?'

'Yes please.'

'Vodka-Martini?'

'Lovely. Shaken, not stirred!'

'Of course!' Delivered beautifully with a selection of hors-d'oeurves.

Also in the bar is one of the reps from another holiday firm. She is around fifty-two, but looks ten years younger and is really nice. The bar manager talks to me for a few minutes and then he says, 'I'm going to get some tablets. I have a really bad headache.'

'Come here, I'll fix it for you.' I say.

'How?'

'Sit down.' He does as I ask and I set about massaging his neck and face. After ten minutes I am finished. 'O.k. how's that? Don't get up too quickly.'

He stands up and seems to be in a complete stupor. He wanders around slightly aimlessly and looks disorientated. For a moment I wonder what I have done to him. I massaged him instinctively and hope I've not done him any damage!

Eventually he announces. 'My headache is gone, how did you do that?'

Phew, relief, I haven't killed him! 'Instinct,' I reply.

He is amazed, and starts telling everyone I have cured his headache. 'You really are a witch,' he announces!

The rep that is also in the bar is fascinated. 'Can you fix my neck and back?'

'I'll try.' I start to massage her neck and shoulder. It is really knotted and I tell her. 'I'll have a go at it, but you have a very old injury here. Really you need a few treatments to make it better. I'll do my best, but you must do what I say to make it better.'

'O.k.' She tells me she has never seen the bar manager look the way he did after my massage. She has known him for seven years and has never seen him ignore people who walk through the bar like he did when I was massaging his neck and head. If I can do this to him she is sure I can fix her neck!

I spend around twenty minutes giving her a really strong massage. The fact that it is so hot helps and I am able to generate an awful lot of heat into her neck and shoulders. When I have finished, for a couple of minutes, I rest one hand just above her head and one just away from her back. When I stop she asks me what I have just done as she has suddenly gone really hot.

'I've just given you some heat back to help you.'

'Oh.'

I explain that she needs to stay very warm this evening, and despite the temperature she must have a hot bath, and sleep preferably on her back. She must wear a T-shirt or something in bed. She promises to follow my instructions.

During this time Michael has arrived, and waits patiently for me. Actually I think he is a little bit prickly at having been ignored for ten minutes. Still he can always look in the mirror if he gets bored!

We go to eat. During the course of our meal, my friends speak to me and it is quite clear Michael is not impressed. He hates being ignored and not being the centre of attention. However, I enjoy his company, and am grateful for his help during my stay. I give him a bottle of wine as a thank-you. I have to admit though that by now I really prefer to eat alone. This is a complete surprise given that less than two weeks ago I was so scared of eating alone. How things change. Afterwards we go for a drink at one of the bars and later I am escorted back to the hotel. Polite, he remains as ever, the perfect gentleman. I retire to the piano bar for cocktail. Tonight's is one he made for a competition. Very refreshing.

TIME TO GO HOME

Friday. Oh no, it's my last day here. I can't believe where the time has gone. Still, I am not going to get depressed until I really have to. I will pretend this is just the same as any other day and not think every routine I follow will be my last.

I go for a walk alone after breakfast and arrive back around eleven o'clock. I walk through the bar and am told once again how bad the golf has been, and am given the blame. I have a glass of water and then head off to the terrace to relax. On the way I meet the rep I gave the massage to the other night.

'How are you?' I ask.

'Great, thanks.'

'How's the shoulder?'

'Wonderful, I've still got a bit of pain in my neck but my back and shoulder are fine. I did what you said and I had the best night's sleep I've had in years. When my partner came back I was fast asleep. Normally we talk for a while before we go to sleep, but he couldn't wake me!'

'Do you want me to have a look at your neck?'

'Have you got time?'

'Of course.' We go to the back of the bar where it is private and I massage her neck.

'You know you have a real gift for this,' she says 'you should do it for a living.'

'I would love to, but I'm not qualified.'

'Don't let that stop you, the reps here would queue for a massage.'

'Yes, but if anything happened I have no insurance and I wouldn't take the risk. Doing it for no payment is o.k. but if you start taking money you really need to be qualified and insured.'

'You should train then. You really are good.'

'Thing is I would be worried that I would lose my instinct if I was trained.'

'I'm sure you wouldn't. It would only enhance your natural ability. You could come and work out here!'

After I had finished, she invited me for a coffee at a bar just outside the hotel. Michael's colleague joins us. As we chat I suddenly find they are joining me for dinner. I don't know how it happened. Actually, I do. I invited the rep I have massaged to join me. Next thing the other girl finds out and she is invited. Damn! I only invited one of them, but I think oh well, at least I can lose them later in the bar.

We agree to meet at seven thirty. For my last night, I wear the black crepe dress, trimmed with gold. I meet them in the bar at seven thirty as arranged for an aperitif. As we chat a man comes to talk. It transpires he is the hotel manager. He joins us for a drink and the next thing I know he is also joining me for dinner. Trouble is we won't all fit around my small table. Flattered that so many people want to eat with me, I am also disappointed that I won't be eating at my table and also that I will miss my friends whose company I have come to enjoy, as well as the young man who has now become my own personal waiter. Oh well, go with the flow. That is what I have been doing for the last few weeks now. Following my nose and so far I haven't been disappointed. As we enter the restaurant all eyes fall upon us. The waiters bustle around and a large round table is presented.

We sit. I am opposite the manager, the two girls either side. Wine is ordered and our food chosen. We exchange pleasantries for a while and then the older rep asks me,

'Will you ask this man why he won't let anyone into the tower?' She has heard from the bar manager of our conversations, and believes I can answer a question for her. She has worked as a rep in this hotel for seven years. Her partner worked in the restaurant for some years, and during all this time she has asked the manager to take her into the tower that symbolises this hotel. He always refuses politely but without any real explanation, other than the steps are very dangerous. Everyone is fascinated as to why no one is allowed there.

I look at him and smile. 'Do you want me to tell them?' I ask.

He smiles and shrugs his shoulders.

'Are you sure?'

With a slightly dismissive nod he gestures o.k.

It is clear to me, and especially having never met me before, he believes I have no idea as to why he won't let anyone into the tower.

I look at him and say. 'Because it's the only place he has control.'

He looks taken aback. The girls are puzzled. 'What do you mean they ask?'

I ask him, 'Shall I tell them?'

Slightly less sure this time he says 'o.k.'

I answer, ' It is the only place you have that is private.'

He nods, but by now I realise he is becoming uncomfortable.

The girls aren't quite with it. 'What is up there?'

'Nothing' I reply.

'How do you know?'

'I just do'

They are puzzled, but I say no more other than to explain that there is nothing sinister up there. They accept my explanation, and he starts to relax, but doesn't take is eyes off me all night. He knows I know his secret, such that it is, without having told me.

We eat our food amidst polite conversation and I go to see my friends on the terrace and take a few photographs of them and the waiter and restaurant manager who have served me so well. The restaurant manager tells me 'I wish I could have had a drink with you one evening. Thing is, I don't think my wife would have approved. He gives me his e-mail address and says he hopes I return. My waiter gives me his address and asks me to send a copy of the photograph. I give him some cigarettes as a tip, and a promise to see everyone at breakfast.

Back with my guests, we retreat to the bar. Things really do become very hectic now. My English friends want to have a drink with me. The bar manager has made me promise to share a champagne cocktail with him, and Piero is coming to my room at midnight. I feel like Cinderella.

Whilst with my dinner guests the hotel manager sits on my left, the two girls are on my right. He leans towards me and says quietly, 'I would like to talk to you alone.'

Yes, and I bet you want to know if I like champagne too, I think to myself!

'Why?'

'I want to know what you think.'

'I can tell you that now.' I turn to the older rep that is sitting next to me. 'Don't leave me with him on my own.' I whisper. She acknowledges with a glance.

I tell him that I believe that although he is the manager of the hotel, he doesn't feel as though he has total control. The tower is where his apartment is and is his only place of sanctuary. He agrees and then goes on to tell me all the problems he has in running the hotel.

'What should I do?' he asks.

'Well, if you are really unhappy move, otherwise stay and persevere. You have a beautiful hotel with a fantastic history. It is almost alive and has to be nurtured along gently.'

Eventually, I make my excuse to move. I arrive at the bar for my champagne cocktail. It is as beautiful as ever and I thank the bar manager for looking after me so well. I give him my book as a gift and leave a message inscribed inside 'Always look after the spirits and the spirits will look after you!'

He laughs and gives me a cocktail menu, which he signs as a memento. Then he looks at me and says 'You know, I could really do it with you.' Call me stupid, or maybe it was his accent, but I hadn't got the faintest idea of what he was on about!

'Do what?'

'You know, "It."'

'What's "It"'

Suddenly I realise! It's sex again, or "champagne" as I now call it!

Completely surprised, and taken aback, I have been totally unaware of this. I give him a friendly slap on the arm and laugh. (How to shatter elegant woman of the world image in one moment!) 'What sort of a girl do you think I am?'

'You have completely turned me upside down,' he says, 'that's why I haven't been able to play golf.'

I realise now he is not joking, and also understand all the references to the golf swing comments he has been making. 'I am really sorry I didn't mean to upset you.'

'I know. Have you enjoyed your stay here?'

'Yes, it's the best thing I've ever done. Thank you for looking after me so well.'

'Pleasure. You will come down tomorrow before you leave?'

'Of course, will you be here?'

'Yes.'

I return to my dinner guests with a quick look at my watch. Eleven forty five. Thanking them all for their company, I make my excuses and leave. I managed to fit in a chat with my friends in the lounge on my way to the ladies, and we agree to meet at breakfast.

I arrive back in my room, just before pumpkin time, and soon after Piero arrives. He has been to my room several times over the course of the last two weeks and he has told me a lot about his life and family. My first impression has not changed. I have a lot of time for his determination and clear vision of what he wants out of life. I know by now that he really likes Islay whisky and give him a bottle as a way of thanks for all the cocktails, bottles of water, beautiful meal, and good company he has provided so discretely for me during my stay. We talk long into the night and drink wine by the window overlooking this magical lake. A perfect end to a perfect holiday.

Next morning, I go to breakfast really early. I want to savour this morning before I have to leave. I chat to the waiters and take a few more photographs before my friends start to arrive. We chat and linger over coffee and I get up to go to the ladies. 'I'll be back in a couple of minutes.'

When I get back, my friend the judge is waiting. 'He thought you'd gone without saying goodbye.' My friends say. His face lights up and he rises to greet me. A kiss on either cheek and we exchange good wishes. He asks me if I will be back next year. I tell him I hope so.

I leave the restaurant for the last time.

My friends have offered me the use of their room to freshen up later. My coach arrives early afternoon so I still have time for a lie in the sun. I return to my room. Check I have left nothing and with one more look out at the lake, I leave.

Later in the morning I go to the bar. On the way I see the older rep. We have a chat and she asks me what the manager was talking about. Nothing much, I tell her. I was just a bit nervous of him. She reminds me to consider my massage qualification and says her shoulder and neck have not felt so good in years.

In the bar I have a coffee and a chat with the bar manager. He gives me the address of where he will be working in London in the winter and phone number and address of where he stays. He asks me to go for a drink if I get the opportunity. With a hug and a kiss on both cheeks, I leave.

After relaxing by the lake I say goodbye to the pool attendant and I go to freshen up. And the next moment the coach is there waiting for me. I want to cry. My friends are with me. They go home in four days time. 'Please don't make me go.' I plead, but as we all know, I have to. They wave me off and I feel terrible. I am so close to tears all the way to the airport. I reapply my make up to pass the time, and next thing I am on the plane, sitting on the runway. Delayed because of a baggage problem, my torture increases. After an hour, the doors close and we are heading back home. Life will never be the same again. I know this, but am not sure what will happen next.

BACK HOME

Christine meets me at the airport. Sad to be home, but nice to be met, we return to her house where her partner is cooking for us. He is a good cook and as ever comes up with the perfect recipe for the moment. He cooks me an Italian dish and we drink Italian wine. I bore them stupid with all the details of my holiday and am not put off as they yawn, fall asleep, and almost die of boredom. (Although I think the latter is rather rude.)

I show Christine the goodies I have collected on my travels and we go to bed.

Next morning, I drive to work. Excited at my adventures I bore everyone there as well! Including Jacqueline, who smugly tells me 'Naaa, told you so. You said you wanted to go on an adventure holiday, well you certainly did that!

Three weeks later, I am walking back to the office after lunch. The sun is shining and it is a glorious day. Just before I reach the door I meet Tim. He works for me on my section. We stop to chat.

'Hiya boss, how are you?'

'Fine thanks, you?'

'Yeah. You know it's great to see you looking so well. Everyone says how good you are looking. Not that you looked bad before, but that holiday really did you so much good. I'm really pleased you enjoyed it so much. You seem so much more relaxed and happy. You deserve it.' As he is speaking, I feel tears welling up in my eyes. 'What's wrong?'

'You're right, I am feeling great, and I had such a wonderful time, but the trouble is I really miss it.'

'I know, but we all get depressed after a good holiday, you'll be all right when you get back into the routine again.'

'That's the trouble Tim, I don't want to, and I can't. I just want to be back there.'

'You really mean that don't you?'

'Yes.'

'Well go back then.'

'What?'

'Go back then.'

'But the trouble is, I came out on such a high I don't think it would be right to go back so soon. Although I am sure they would be great to me, it wouldn't have the same impact as last time.'

'Go somewhere else then.'

'I don't know.'

'What have you got to lose?'

'I know, but I had such a lovely time there, it could never be that good again.'

'Look, you went there with no expectations, and look what happened.'

'True, and the trouble is if I don't go again soon, I think I'll lose my confidence to do it again.'

'Have you got plenty of annual leave?'

'Loads.'

'What have you got to lose then? We can manage without you. Go and book it and get yourself off there again.'

I spend some time thinking about it. If I don't go away again on my own, I may never go again, or at least I may only retain the confidence to go to this one place. I realise I do need to go somewhere else in order to keep the doors of my solitary travelling life open. This is not just an issue of having another holiday, it's about pushing back the walls that threaten to close in and squeeze all the confidence out of me.

I am not sure if this applies to everyone, but in terms of fear, I'll tell you my theory on it and my interpretation of how I visualise it.

We all have fears of one form or another. For me every fear is a brick wall. It is circular and surrounds me completely. There are no windows or doors and no roof. I am always looking down at myself in the middle of these walls from above. Depending on how big the fear is, depends on how high the wall is and how tightly it surrounds me. The more fears I have, the more walls I have. The other problem is that they are never static. Always moving, they are constantly forming a tighter and tighter circle around me. So even the relatively small fears I have grow as these circles tighten. Some fears I have had in my life have been things that I cannot, or feel unable to, solve at a particular moment. With these walls the best I can do is put all my weight behind them and push them back to a distance that stops me being suffocated. When I am so tired of pushing or feel I really do have to demolish one of my walls the only solution is to smash them down with my fists, and this for me is the only way to win the war of fear. If you allow it to consume you, you miss out on the bountiful and glorious pleasures that there are to be found beyond. I know this because I have found so many wondrous treasures beyond my walls it gives me the courage to keep on fighting.

Later that afternoon, my mind is made up. I go off to the travel agents.

'I want to go away again.'

'Great, where do you want to go?'

'Back to the same lake but a different place, know anywhere?'

We get out the brochures and start our search. It is not easy. This is now the height of the season and the hotels are all full. We try many different holiday companies, and search for flights. Strangely the one place that keeps coming up with a single room is the place I have just returned from. But I have made up my mind, and am not going to return there. After an hour and a quarter, we have tried every lake and every four star hotel. I decide it is not going to happen and tell her to leave it.

'Let me just try one more company. They are a specialist Italian holiday firm.' By now I am going off the idea. Even the four star hotels, beautiful though they are, don't appeal to me. But since she has spent so long looking for me I agree for her to check.

She finds a few and I eventually choose one. She phones the tour operator. They have a room and a flight, do I want it?

Deep breath again. 'O.k. Book it!'

I ask her whether she knows anyone who has stayed in this hotel.

'I have booked people into it, but no one has ever come back to tell me about it. But this is probably because it is so good. Very often people don't bother to tell me if it is good, only if they are complaining. I'm sure it's fine, it's a four star hotel after all.'

'I know. It's just that last time you chose it and knew it was good. This time I have chosen it and I feel less certain about it.'

'Don't worry I'm sure it will be fine. Look it has everything you want, including fourteen acres of grounds with lakes and swimming pool. It's only for a week. Do what you did last time. Take your book and enjoy the sunshine.'

RIVA DEL GARDA

'Tim, what are you doing the ninth of September?'

'Nothing, as far as I know.'

'Great, will you take me to Manchester airport?'

'I should have known you wanted something! Yeah, no probs, I'll check with my girlfriend, make sure she's got no plans. In fact she'll probably drive!'

'Thanks, I know it's a bit of a cheek, but after all it was your idea for me to go back!'

'Remind me to keep my mouth shut in future! How are you getting back?'

'My sister is fetching me.'

I pack my case again and after dropping my car at my sister's house we travel to Manchester airport where I am dropped at departures and waved off. This time I check in alone. (How grown up am I!)

As we hurtle down the runway, I realise I am alone again, and this time it is infinitely worse than last time. Last time I had no expectations. This time my expectations have a minus value. I expect I will be unhappy as the place, the people, the hotel, the room, the view in fact everything, don't match up to the last holiday. I can't imagine anything being as good as that, and console myself with the idea that as long as I can come back with the idea that I can still travel alone, I will have succeeded in my mission.

At least the airport is familiar and after collecting my luggage I walk through to arrivals and see someone holding a placard with my name on.

I am led to a car and soon realise that I am being taken to my hotel on my own, by private taxi. 'Ooh' I think, this is not so bad, better than stopping at half a dozen other hotels on the way. The journey takes about an hour.

Riva is at the very north of the lake and nestles between the mountains at the Lake's source. My previous hotel is south of the lake where the valley mellows towards its plain. As we travel through the various villages en route, I relax a little. The lake looks as beautiful as I remember and as we get closer to Riva the mountains become dominant and comforting as they wrap their stony arms around the lake's edge.

Sooner than I imagine, I am there. My luggage is collected and I walk up the steps, and through the circular automatic doors finding myself in the reception area.

Very different, this hotel is much more modern and feels more corporate and professional than the family feeling of the other one. I give a tip to the driver and I walk to the reception counter.

Hmm, I don't like this much. The reception counter is exceptionally high, very unwelcoming and I feel like a Chad as I struggle to fit my chin over the top of it. I wonder who on earth designed this? The staff however, are friendly and after the preliminaries are over I am taken to my room. Room number two-six-two. Spooky! The room number at the other hotel was two-two-six!

Back to the old routine, check the bathroom, spotless. Sterilised toilet, (comes as standard!) Huge shower, beautiful. No complaints here. Room, plain but plenty of room and a walk in wardrobe. So far so good.

Now to the view. I open the blind and draw back the curtain. Pretty damn good. I am facing the front of the hotel overlooking the hotel car park, but beyond that is a mountain, on the top of which sits a red and white striped radio mast. True it's not like looking out across the lake, but I am pleased all the same. Call to Christine and Jane. Everything o.k. so far. But.......What to wear!

We decide on the ivory shift dress and devore over-shirt. With my tan this dress looks good. Gold high shoes and gold bag. Make up to match. I spend an hour getting ready, one last check in the mirror and, hand on the door, I take a deep breath. Here goes...Again.

I walk down the stairs and turn left. The restaurant is directly at the end of a long walkway. Either side, are comfortable modern sofas and armchairs in navy or cream, with low glass topped coffee tables. At the end, to the right of the restaurant is a bar, and a grand piano sits opposite. I am slightly confused by all of this, as this walkway is obviously a main thoroughfare through the hotel. I wonder if there is another bar, as this seems rather busy and disjointed.

Two steps up to the restaurant and walking carefully throughout I stand near the entrance and wait.

The room is very big, square and bright. Decorated in a soft green and white, it is very modern but very nice. Divided every so often by trellis screens and plants, it makes it feel more intimate than it would otherwise be. The middle of the ceiling is painted to resemble looking up into a conservatory. The whole effect is very nice and feels fresh and clean.

MARIO

The restaurant is very busy. There are many waiters in their white jackets, dickey bows, and black trousers, and three or four men in black jackets. These must be the senior staff. I notice one of them. He has very dark hair and is very attractive.

Within a couple of minutes another of these men approaches me. I give him my room number and he shows me to a table. He is the restaurant manager. He hands me a menu with a smile, and leaves me.

I am comfortable at my table. I am sitting with one of the screens behind me and feel safe. I peruse the menu. Three courses and a sweet.

Next thing the man I noticed earlier is standing next to me. He really is attractive with a very soft smile and gentle manner. I give him my order and ask him for a nice white wine. He returns and as we exchange pleasantries, he stares at me. Undaunted by this I look straight back at him. Throughout the evening, he comes to me often, invariably not saying anything, but with arms folded, head to one side and a half smile, he just stares at me and sighs. I find this very amusing, (and flattering, of course!) and smiling, I stare right back.

At the end of my main course, he asks me if I want a sweet. It is another table in the middle of the room, and I politely refuse. He asks me 'Would you like me to take something for you?'

'Yes please, but just a small amount.' He returns with a few sweets on a plate. They are delicious. I ask him when is the quietest time to eat and he tells me around eight thirty.

Finishing my meal, I decide I have to go and sit in the bar, same as last time. I ask him 'Can you tell me where the bar is please?'

'Certainly,' He takes my chair, and escorts me out of the restaurant. The bar is outside, where I had seen it before and he confirms this is the only one. I thank him and order a drink. I sit down with my book.

Surprise, surprise, it's Bridget Jones Diary! I never got to finish it last time, being overtaken by events. I bought a new copy at the airport and I start to read again. All the time I am watching and taking note of my new surroundings. At around eleven thirty I retire to bed. First day over and all in all, not nearly as bad as I expected.

Next day I meet the rep in the hotel reception. She is very helpful and tells me I am staying in the best hotel in Riva. I ask her a few pointers, like which way is the town, how far, etc. and she asks me if I want to go on any excursions. I decline telling her I just want to relax by the pool, walk and look at the lake. She leaves me her details and goes.

I go to find the pool. The gardens to the hotel are magnificent and extensive. Hiding beneath trees and amidst three lakes I find it. It is superb, and with so much space in the gardens, it is possible to find somewhere very quiet, or stay around the edge of the pool. I take a bed at the edge of the pool and lie for a while before going for a swim. There is also a children's pool and I notice there are many families staying here, and the age range is much broader than before. Later in the afternoon, I walk to the end of the gardens, which lead to the lake.

The view is wonderful. The water, crystal clear and absolutely alive, chatters with excitement and expectation as it begins its infant journey southwards. Such is the vibrancy of this water, as I look down the lake my thoughts are swept from my mind and whisked away almost before I have time to see them. I find it hard to imagine the difference at the other end of the lake. I am told it takes three years for the water to travel from one end to the other, and I can see that by the time it reaches the southern end of the lake, it has matured and experienced life. Quiet and serene it basks in the warmth and comfort of its dotage. Softened by age there is no need to rush any more. Time to relax and enjoy the memories of its life journey.

I turn and follow the winding path along the lake that leads to the town. The town is very old with narrow streets leading off a square. I realise that this was a good decision to come here and know I am going to enjoy my stay.

Returning to the hotel I prepare for dinner. Call to Christine, and tonight it's the navy Escada dress.

I walk down to dinner and take my place at the table. The same man attends me as last night. Again all evening he keeps coming to me, stares at me and sighs.

'Why do you keep staring at me?' I ask.

'It's your eyes.'

'And you're Italian!'

'No, really you have fascinating eyes' (He'll be offering champagne next!)

As the evening passes I know without any doubt that he will ask me out. I decide when he does that I will go. After all if I don't like it I don't have to go again. I finish my meal and make to leave. It is around ten o'clock. He comes over to me and asks,

'Would you consider going for a drink with me later this evening?'

I pause for a moment. 'O.k.'

'Really? My manager said you would never come!'

'Tell him he was wrong!'

'I finish at ten thirty. I'll meet you on the car park.'

'Where about? The car park is quite big.'

'Don't worry, I'll find you!'

I skip back to my room, cleverly disguised as a walk, and wonder whether I should change. I decide not to and taking a silk shawl, I walk out of my room a couple of minutes after ten thirty, and arrive at the top of the steps at ten thirty five. As I walk down I see his silhouette near the entrance gate. I walk towards him slowly.

'Would you like to walk along the lake into Riva?'

'Lovely.'

'Are you o.k. to walk in your shoes?'

'Yes no problem.' We turn to walk along the side of the hotel.

'My name is Mario,' he says.

I never thought to ask him his name! He wore a name badge, but as Maitre D it shows only his surname.

'My name is Gill.'

'Gill?' He seems to struggle with it and it suddenly sounds very strange.

'Well, actually it's Gillian, but people tend to call me Gill.'

'Gillian.'

There are, I am afraid certain limitations to words on paper. This is one of those 'had to be there moments,' and as much as I would like to, it is impossible to explain just how beautiful my name sounded when he said it. Soft and romantic, this is the first time in my thirty-eight years that hearing my name said in full didn't make me feel that I was in trouble for some misdemeanour.

As we walk, I try to tell him in five minutes about my previous holiday, and why I had come back. Impossible and even as I spoke it sounded like I had been released from some home for the not quite right brigade. Brain in top gear, mouth in reverse, he admits later he thought I was a bit weird!

We stroll along the winding path and every now and again he stops and looks out across the lake. 'Do you like the lake?' he asks.

'It is beautiful.'

'I like it too. I never feel able to stay away from this lake for too long.' We maintain eye contact and at this moment I know we have something lovely in common, even if our verbal language may fail sometimes. (Well, quite often actually!)

I notice he wears a Russian wedding ring and I ask him is he married.

'Yes, and I have a son who is eight years old.'

'Doesn't your wife mind you taking another woman out for a drink?'

'We are separated. We have never got around to getting divorced, but we have been separated for three years.'

'I'm sorry.'

'Ah well, this is the life sometimes.'

We walk into the town and he offers me his arm as I tiptoe over the cobbles in the middle of the square. He takes me for a walk around and tells me the local history, and then we go to a bar to drink. He orders a glass of red wine each, and we sit on a pair of high stools. As I take the weight off my feet, they start to pound and throb, and I wonder how on earth I am going to walk back! I take off my shawl and fold it up. He watches fascinated as this voluminous piece of fabric diminishes to the size of a ladies handkerchief and slips inside my small handbag.

'It's silk, and folds up really small.' I say, smiling.

'It's beautiful. Do you mind if I smoke?' he asks.

'No, you carry on.' And I then go on to give him a lecture about smoking and the fact that his son will be really upset if his father dies at a young age. This is the second time in less than an hour that mouth and brain have been out of sync! He puts his cigarette back in the packet and I feel really guilty.

'Really I don't mind if you smoke.' I say

' No, it's o.k.'

'Honestly, please, I really don't mind. I didn't mean to give you a lecture.'

'No. You're right. I really should try to stop.' At this point I take the packet from him and light a cigarette for him. 'Please, I really don't mind.'

We start to talk, and very soon he tells me all about himself. He tells me his father died a few weeks ago, and he is clearly still feeling very raw at this loss. He goes on to tell me almost everything about his life while I sit and listen quietly. It also becomes apparent to me that he has many issues in his life that he is struggling with. During the rest of this evening I talk very little, but listen intently, as he pours out his story. Later, I realise that this evening forms the foundation of our friendship to come.

Sometime later we move to another bar and I ask him why he kept staring at me in the restaurant.

'It is your eyes.'

'Oh yes, I've heard that before.'

'No really, they are like a serpent's eyes.'

'What do you mean?'

'They keep your gaze, so that you can't look away, and you seem to see straight into my soul.'

Eventually it is time to walk back. As I stand, it feels like every ounce of blood in my body has fallen to my feet, they are really hurting. Not wishing to lose my composure I say nothing, and after a few minutes the pain doesn't feel so bad.

As we draw near to the hotel he stops and kisses me. He asks me if I want to go back to his room with him. I am not sure, and we spend some time debating the issue. I don't want to feel that every time I go away on my own I start jumping into bed with a man I don't know. However, I make a decision and decide to go with him.

We walk back into the hotel, which by now is sleeping. Only the night receptionist is there. A long walk through the hotel we arrive at his room. He opens the door and I go in.

'Wow, it's beautiful.'

'Thank you.'

The walls are covered in oil paintings and I soon find out he has painted them. Colourful and well defined, they are beautiful. I am fascinated by them.

He opens his small fridge and opens a bottle of wine. Then he puts on some music. It is beautiful and something I haven't heard before.

We go on to discuss music, and as the week goes by, discover we share a lot of the same taste and we both love music.

As a child both my parents enjoyed music, and we had a radio in every room in the house. I have gone on to enjoy all sorts of music and could not imagine life without it. I think there is often a certain amount of snobbery attached to it. For me, I like what I like, and what I listen to goes with my mood at the time. Mario and I have shared some lovely times listening to music.

We sit on the bed and drink and talk and then just sit and stare into each other's eyes. Eventually we go to bed and sleep comfortably.

Monday. At six-thirty in the morning he gets up to go to work. Whilst he is in the bathroom I start to get up. He hears me and says, 'Please, you stay here and sleep a while. Go back to your room later.' Setting the alarm for later he leaves quietly and I go back to sleep.

Rising at around eight-thirty, I dress and go back to my room. I suddenly feel conspicuous. I am dressed in my evening dress and have to walk the gauntlet, back to my room at the other end of the hotel, passing everyone who will be going to breakfast! As I descend the stairs, an elderly couple walk behind me. Not realising I am English, she says to her husband, 'looks like she had a good night last night!'

I turn and smile. 'Yes, I did!' I reply.

Embarrassment over, I walk back to my room seeing no one else.

Washed and changed I go to breakfast. My feet are killing me and I find it very uncomfortable to walk. I think that during the night someone swapped my feet for an elephant's. They feel really heavy. Pounding my way to the restaurant, I take a seat. My coffee is delivered with flowers adorning the saucer. Mario comes to see me and asks if I am all right.

'Fine, thank you.' I reply.

After breakfast I decide that I will have to do something to relieve the pounding in my feet. I go down to the lake and dip my feet in the water. It is freezing! But the relief is almost instant, and after twenty minutes by which time any pain has become numbed by the cold water, I return to the pool to soak up some sun, swim, read my book and catch up on some sleep. Pure bliss!

Returning to my room, I feel relaxed and comfortable. Then I do something that I never normally do. I switch on the television. Scrolling through the channels, I come across the American news channel CNN. I can't believe my eyes or ears as I see the twin towers falling. It is September the eleventh 2001, and like the rest of the world, I am shocked into disbelief at the events unfolding. It is made even more unbelievable for me being in a foreign country, watching an American T.V news channel. Watching events unfold, the awful truth and grim sight is like watching a film. I find it difficult to imagine that this is not an American disaster movie.

Almost impossible to believe I call Jane and then Christine. Yes it is true. The world is in a state of shock.

Struggling to know what to say, and feeling like any other topic of conversation is in such bad taste and disrespectful I find it difficult to tell her about the previous evening. Eventually however, knowing I still have to eat despite this terrible tragedy, I decide to wear the black dress, with the gold trim that I bought on my last holiday. Leaving my room, I start to walk to the restaurant, not knowing what to expect. As I walk in and take my place there is a very strange atmosphere in the room. Everyone seems frightened to talk let alone laugh or smile. The staff are wonderful. Business as usual, but with an air of deference.

I find I am sitting at a table next to another English couple and we start to chat. Naturally, the main topic of conversation is of America, but after a while the conversation changes and moves on. Mindful of events and respectful but again the disbelief seems to make it acceptable to talk of other issues and this seems to be the feeling throughout the restaurant that everyone has.

They are 'people watchers' and tell me that they find the attention I am receiving highly amusing. They ask me a little about myself and it transpires that they also live in the Midlands. They know where I live and then ask what I do for a living. I make them promise not to blow my cover and they are in fits of laughter when they know I work for the Benefits Agency.

'Were you by the pool today?' Mario asks.

'Yes, why?'

'I asked the attendant to give you a message.'

'No one spoke to me.'

'No worry, I was just going to ask if you wanted to come to my room, but I think you would prefer to be by the pool.'

'If I had known, I would have come.'

'Really?'

'Yes.'

Would you like to go out again this evening?'

'That would be lovely.'

'If you have something else to do…'

'No. I don't.'

I'll call you when I finish. Would you like a sweet?'

'No, thank you. I really am full.'

'How about strawberries?'

'Oh o.k. then.' And so, in this hotel, from this night, I always have strawberries.

Later he calls me and I walk to his room. This evening we go to a bar in Limone. What a change from the last time I was here as I remember Limone is where I met the couple when I was staying in the other hotel and where I felt so ill. I wonder if they are still serving toasties in their hotel! The bar is absolutely heaving with people, but everyone is so friendly and the atmosphere is wonderful. We dance together, and have a really fun evening. Returning to his room we talk long into the night.

In the morning he goes to work early again and I lie in. When I wake I spend a long time looking at the beautiful paintings that adorn his room. There are two that particularly captivate me. One is a large picture of a man and is framed on his wall. I sense an awful lot of emotion has been put into this painting. The other is some sort of much smaller abstract picture which I really like.

Eventually I have to go back to my room and prepare for breakfast. Once again I walk rather conspicuously back to my room but again I see no one on the way. At breakfast, I am treated with extra care, flowers folded in my napkin, fresh orange juice and a strawberry on the side of my coffee cup.

'Would you like to come to my room this afternoon?'

'Yes, lovely.'

'I will finish around two-thirty. Don't hurry back from whatever you do, I'll call you again if you are not back.'

'Fine,' I say nonchalantly. My head shouting, you must be joking, I'll be in my room at two- thirty!

I leave breakfast and go for a walk to the lake. Later I lie by the pool, swim and sleep. By two-thirty, I am back in my room. Good timing since the sun is really hot now. My phone rings shortly.

This afternoon he takes me for a drive into the mountains behind Riva. It is beautiful, narrow twisting roads with horseshoe bends, creeping gracefully through the small villages the hug the hillside. We stop and walk a while, before returning to the hotel.

In the evening I go to eat. During my meal a middle-aged man comes over to me. 'My wife thinks your clothes are fantastic. Where do you get them from?'

'Thank you. A little shop near where I live.'

'She made me take her shopping today to buy her some clothes to wear in the restaurant. You have cost me a fortune!'

'Sorry! But I am sure she deserves it'

He starts to ask me about myself. 'Why are you alone? Are you here on business?'

'Well, you know...'

'I knew you were. What do you do?'

'I work for the government.'

'Ah, do you deal in finance?'

'Well....'

'I knew it. I'll have a chat with you about investments sometime.'

'Right.'

He leaves. The couple I am sitting near are nearly choking.

'Don't tell him will you? I ask them. 'I won't lie to him, but let's just see what else he assumes.'

'O.k.'

Mario has not missed this encounter. He tells me many people are interested to know who I am.

Later that evening, I meet Mario and he takes me to a bar in the mountains. It's very old and rustic, and again the view across the lake is beautiful. With the streetlights twinkling along the edge of the lake, and the moon casting its soft light on the water which is very tranquil, it all looks very romantic.

Wednesday. After breakfast, I go to the lake. Last night when we were talking, Mario told me how difficult his life is for him sometimes. I know he is sensitive, and the loss of his father so recently has made everything ten times worse. Ask him what he wants most in the world, and the answer is always the same, (even when he is very drunk!) "Peace for everybody in the world."

I tell him. 'Everyone has a path of life, and for every person this path is unique. We can never share our path with another and we each form our own. When we are born, our path stretches out emptily and expectant, the possibilities are abounding. For some people their path is hard, dry and made of rough concrete. The sun beats down unrelentingly and there is no shelter to be found.

For others the path is very beautiful. It is lush and green and has a beautiful crystal clear stream flowing through it. There are white lilies in beautiful bloom floating gently on its surface, and fish swim happily in its depth. Up above in the trees birds sing happily, and the sun shines beautifully, filtering its way through to produce a dappled light that gently kisses the undergrowth. The trees grow strong and tall. The flora and fauna thrive. Their lives travel alongside nature, never compete, and they appreciate the beauty as well as never underestimating its power.

The problem with this is those people with a less beautiful path see it and don't like it. Becoming jealous they will try to spoil things, build a dam and interrupt the flow of water, suffocating the whole life force from this equatorial heaven.

When we meet someone we like, we can steer our life so that it runs alongside another. Our paths may have many branches, that reflect different aspects of our life, but the only single thing everyone's path has in common, is that you can never walk on anyone else's. You can however, make your path as beautiful and bountiful as you like. It costs no money, only kindness, compassion, courtesy and honesty. The more you give, the more beautiful it becomes. In the end, life and your path, is often what you make it.

Another story I tell is 'You can never hold a bird in your hand. If you try, as soon as it gets the chance it will fly, and never return. All you can do is to hold out your hand, and hope that one day a bird will land there. Keeping your hand still and always open the bird may stay a while. At some point it will fly away. This is where trust comes. You stay patiently, and hope that it will return to perch again. The more open your hand the more often it will return to perch. But you also have to know that every bird needs to fly. That's what they do. When you try to hold it by force, it will quickly die. Always stay true to yourself. We cannot be what everyone wants us to be, we are all individual and everyone wants something different of us. This is impossible to achieve. Be yourself and then they will either take you or leave you. Being true to yourself, means being honest with yourself, and those around you. Easy to say, but sometimes incredibly difficult to do.'

I continue. 'The only thing I ask of you, and of anyone who knows me, is to always be honest. I don't care what you tell me, as long as you are honest. I have a strong sense of what people are thinking, and when this is in conflict with what they are saying I become nervous and anxious.'

Mario has many friends, they come from many parts of the globe, and he can be seen as having a very enviable life. In many ways he does. He enjoys his work, and enjoys meeting people.

The down side is long, unsociable hours, living in a small hotel room. At the end of the season he has to pack and move to his winter work. Another hotel, another room to call home for the next few weeks. Not easy, but being so transient seems to enable him to make wherever he is homely, comfortable and cosy. Despite the beautiful rooms in the hotel, Mario's small room, is always more preferable to be.

During this first week, Mario and I talk a lot, and despite our language barrier we are able to establish a bond that was to be the formation of our friendship. In spite of the complexities of our respective lives and backgrounds, we understood each other. It was as simple as that.

Thursday, and Mario has a day off today. He told me last night that he has the afternoon and following day free and normally goes home. He looks slightly pensive.

'Of course you must go home. Your wife and son were in your life before I came along. Your wife is still a very important person in your life and more than that she is the mother of your child. Enjoy your day and I'll see you when you get back.'

'You sure?'

'Positive. You accept me as I am, and I do the same.

'O.k. but I am also free on Friday evening. Would you like to go for a meal with me?'

'That would be lovely.'

'I'll call you when I return. But what about your meal in the restaurant, you have paid for it'

'Don't worry, I would much prefer to eat out with you.'

'Sure.'

'Positive, now go!'

So today, I have the whole day to myself. I go to the pool, swim, sleep and read my book. Guess what, I have almost finished it! Later, when the sun becomes really hot I walk into Riva and do some shopping. Returning to the hotel, I book an appointment for a back massage. Heavenly!

In the evening I go to the restaurant and chat with the people I have become friendly with. Tonight, we are eating in a different restaurant. It is smaller and I am sitting next to the pianist midway in the room.

The man who thinks I am some sort of financial wonder-woman stops at my table for a chat and asks me what I think about the stock market.

'I think it's very up and down.' I reply with a straight face. 'I think property is always the best investment. It may dip now and again, but as long as you can afford the long-term investment, that's where I like to put money.'

'I agree,' he says.

'Of course, a few years ago, it was a good idea to set up a retirement home, but they have taken off so well, there aren't such good opportunities in it now.'

'Yes, yes I'm sure you're right.'

'And with so many building societies converting, anyone who was shrewd enough to speculate there, well that was very good judgement. Of course you always need the money in the first place, but the more you have the better your return.'

'Absolutely!'

Absolute common sense, I think!

As the restaurant empties towards the end of dinner, I start watching the people coming and going to the sweet table in the middle of the room in front of me, I see two middle aged women walking around the table. I also notice the reaction of a couple of waiters and a waitress. They are looking in fascinated disbelief at the hair of these two women, and so am I! One has grey hair and the other red. Both have their hair pulled into spikes and tipped on the ends with black and purple respectively. I have never seen anything like it, and like the staff found it fascinatingly awful!

We all glance at each other and try to stifle muffled titters. Eventually one of the waiters who has also been flirting with me during the week, passes me a piece of paper with a cartoon drawing of these two women as chads, their spiky hair sticking over the wall! We wait until they leave before we all laugh.

Later I go to the bar for a drink. Pleased that I am still able to do this without feeling awkward, I go to bed fairly early to catch up on some sleep.

Friday. My last day here. Oh no! I can't believe where the time has gone. I go through the ritual for one last time. Pool. Swim. Sun. Sleep. Oh and finally, I finish reading my book. Good job really, since I am starting to feel I could write my own version. Only trouble is, that fact is definitely stranger than fiction, they'd never believe it. When the sun gets too hot I return to my room and start to pack. I really hate this.

All my memories of this small moment in time are called to an abrupt end and squashed into a suitcase as the time comes to step back to reality again. But the problem is I know that everything here will still be going on just the same after I leave. The cast are the same, but the audiences are different. I know people will come and go, and the hotel will not distinguish one person from another. The waiters and staff will be polite and friendly to everyone, and every now and then another someone will stand out as different for whatever reason, and maybe go on to form a friendship. How long will it last I wonder. A week, a month, a lifetime, or will it evaporate as soon as the car leaves for the airport? Who knows? Only time will tell…

At six thirty, Mario calls me. 'Still o.k. for tonight?'

'Yes.'

'Seven thirty?'

'Fine, see you later.'

I go down to reception to pay my bill. Then I go to the restaurant to say I will not be eating this evening. I take my bottle of wine that I have left, and leave a tip with the restaurant manager, in an envelope. Taking the bottle of wine I go to Mario's room, for the last time.

We leave shortly afterwards and he takes me to a typical Italian trattoria in the mountains. Old and rustic, as we enter we are greeted by a roaring log fire and long tables either side of the room. The restaurant owner comes to us and after an aperitif Mario orders a typical antipasti dish, followed by a mixed meat platter. It is all delicious, but there is so much I soon start to struggle. Also I am not sure of how to eat some of the food. Struggling to eat a piece of chicken Mario tells me,

'Princess Margaret beats the chicken with her fingers.'

'What!'

'Princess Margaret, she beats the chicken with her fingers.'

Conjuring up an image in my mind, I start to laugh uncontrollably. Anyone who knows me will tell you that when I really laugh, I just can't stop. The more I picture Princess Margaret beating chickens with her fingers, tiara slightly askew, the assembled entourage looking on as if this is a perfectly normal, if somewhat slightly strange, English royal custom, the more I laugh. Eventually, Mario starts to laugh with me, but is still not sure of what is so funny. 'Why are you laughing?' he asks.

'The idea of Princess Margaret beating chickens with her fingers!'

'Not beating. Eating!' This makes me crack up completely! And we don't stop laughing for a good half hour, by which time I can hardly eat anything.

After more wine, and grappa, we eventually leave the restaurant and head back to the hotel. Back in his room we spend a long night speaking very little, listening to music, which accompanies us to sleep.

Next morning, I go down to breakfast for the last time. My taxi is arriving around lunchtime. The waiters, who have become more friendly during the week, say goodbye and tell me they hope I will return soon. I hope so too.

Mario gives me a long look and says he will try to see me before I leave. Returning to my room, I meet the waiter from last night who handed me the cartoon. He is on room service duty and as we walk, we seem to be heading in the same direction. He is very tall, dark, quite handsome, and all week has been asking me to sleep with him, promising me a good time! I have laughed it off, tell him absolutely no chance, and he has taken it with good humour. As we walk, we chat about my going home and how I have really enjoyed my stay here. We end up outside my room. He is delivering to the room opposite. Opening my door with his key, I thank him for his kind attention. He makes to kiss me on either cheek and a hug. Next thing he has me on the bed arms round me offering more than a hug. Completely taken aback, I tell him 'no, no!'

'Really?'

'Really! I am very flattered, but I really don't want to sleep with you!'

'O.k.' and with that he leaves. No harm done and I thought no more of it.

Looking around my room, I check that I have everything. We have been warned of delays at the airport as security is on a high state of alert. We are advised that there are certain items that cannot be taken on board and will have to be put in the hold, including manicure scissors, corkscrews, nail files etc. I put most things in my vanity case and take out my camera, films and other items.

Later, there is a knock at the door, it is Mario. He comes in and we sit on the bed. Again there is very little to say, just an understanding of a special friendship that has been formed. I take a few photographs and he leaves again. I take a deep breath and then go for a walk down to the lake for the last time. I can't believe what a wonderful time I have had, and I know life will never be the same for me again. Fighting back tears I head back to the hotel to wait for my taxi.

Handing in my key, one of the porters asks me if I need my bags collecting from my room. Thanking him I say yes, and we start to talk. He speaks very good English, and asks me if I have had a good time. 'Wonderful.' I respond.

'Will you come back again?'

'I would love to, but I'm not sure whether I can.'

'Everybody likes you here.'

'That's very generous, but I'm sure they like everyone.'

'No, you are different. You are friendly, and kind to everyone.'

'Thank you. Travelling alone is a different experience to travelling with people. You have to make the effort to talk, but it is really easy here since everyone has been friendly towards me.'

'What time is your taxi?'

'Two o'clock.'

'Go and have a cappuccino in the bar, I'll fetch your bags and I'll let you know when your taxi comes.'

'Thank you. That's very kind of you.'

'Pleasure.'

I walk to the bar, and the bar manager calls over to me. 'Coffee?'

'Yes please.'

'Cappuccino?'

'Lovely, thank you.'

Sitting at the bar he delivers my coffee and some biscuits. 'Leaving today?'

'Yes unfortunately.'

'Come back again soon, we like you.'

'Thank you, I'll try!' He carries on with his work, whilst I sip my coffee, Mario suddenly appears. 'Hey. Still here?'

'Yes. The porter is looking out for my taxi. He suggested I come for a coffee. He is really nice. He told me everyone likes me and asked if I was coming back!'

'It's true, everyone does like you. We would all like to see you back again.'

He holds my hand for a moment, then kisses me on the cheek and goes back to work.

The bar manager reappears a few minutes later and as I ask for the bill, he tells me, 'No, have that one on me.'

'Thank you'

I go to the toilet, and then go to reception to wait for my taxi. The porter is still there and keeps me company until my taxi arrives. Taking a long look at the hotel as the taxi draws away I wonder what the future holds.

Driving back along the side of the lake, it still looks beautiful, and I feel as though I am being ripped physically from this place. I had no idea that I would have had such a wonderful time. Arriving at the airport, I am brought back to reality.

The airport is heaving. Verona airport is not very big and chaos seems to be the order of the day. Swarming with soldiers carrying machine guns, no one seems quite sure what to do. I join the queue for check in and am asked to check I have none of the newly banned items in my hand luggage. Thus checked, I wander around waiting for my flight to be called. My first experience of Verona airport warned me not to go through to departures until called, as the departure area is very small and gets very crowded. So, I wait, and wait, and wait. No problem with this since everyone understands the need for vigilance and everyone is patient, although a little bored.

The irony though, is that despite being banned from taking small scissors, corkscrews and nail files, we are still allowed to buy duty free glass bottles of wines and spirits! Presumably terrorists don't buy wine, or if they do, at least they wouldn't have a corkscrew to open the bottle, drink the contents, (or share it with the passengers to avoid spillage,) before thinking to break the bottle and use the resulting glass shards as a lethal weapon. No, I suppose this is something that only happens after a drunken brawl on a Saturday night down the local. Never at 30,000 feet.

The other item I find surprising that I can carry on board is a pair of tweezers! Maybe the threat of being plucked to death is less of a threat, especially on a short haul flight, but I start to worry that in the absence of a corkscrew, the terrorist may be foxy enough to pluck out the cork of the bottle with my tweezers, and then drink us all to death, Worse, they may have been to university and therefore thought to buy a screw top. Whisky galore, they all went down singing!

I know this is very flippant, but as in all the best true stories, it happened. Glass bottles are o.k. Corkscrews and nail files are banned. So we all feel safe. Oh and of course, no metal knives and forks on the plane and no glasses to drink out of. We'll just have to pass round the terrorist's bottle of Lugano instead.

So, having bought my couple of bottles of non-terrorist Lugano, my flight is eventually called and I go through to departures, where I join the heaving throng of waiting passengers. Another check of our hand luggage and the pile of banned items is mounting. I wonder will they melt all these objects down and build some weapons of mass destruction out of the resultant smelt?

110

Again, I wait, and wait, and wait. Eventually, as if to make me feel at home, I look up and see my table companions walk through. They are also flying to Manchester, but on a later flight, two hours later, in fact. They are flying British Airways, I am flying British European, and the race is on... Who will leave first!

After another wait, both planes are on the tarmac. We are both called through to our respective gates and a friendly rivalry ensues. However, they have picked the wrong airline. B.A are frisking all their passengers and checking all their hand luggage. Can't be too careful, there may be a stray pair of eyelash curlers that have escaped detection. So whilst they are frisked, we are whisked, straight onto our waiting plane with only our passports to produce as we board! We made it, and as we hurtle down the runway, they are still boarding. Never mind, we'll probably all end up around the same carousel at Manchester!

Arriving home, I collect my luggage and walk through to arrivals. As I scan the faces I see a hand held up with my name on it. My sister and her boyfriend have driven up to collect me from the airport. Chatting all the way to the car, my sister and I sit in the back together as we travel home. After half an hour or so, I switch on my mobile phone. Within a few minutes, it bleeps as a message arrives.

'Welcome in your home, I think of you'

I am amazed! I didn't really know whether I would hear from Mario again, and smile at his English. Later that evening we chat on the phone for a few minutes, lovely to talk, but difficult to understand. His English is even more difficult to understand on the 'phone, and my Italian stretches to yes, no, and thank you!

Going home the next day, I am filled with delight as I have not only survived, but once again enjoyed another holiday on my own. Self-esteem and confidence rocketing, I feel great!

During the evening my phone rings and it's Mario, we try to chat for a while, but it is really difficult. I realise I am going to have to do something if this friendship is to survive.

After a few days and a dictionary, I am still struggling. I also have lots of annual leave still left and so decide there is only one answer. Another holiday. Only this time I decide to go back to Riva, for two weeks.

I call Mario first to check he doesn't mind me going back. On the contrary, he is really pleased, and before I know it, I am back again. A couple of new dresses bought in the sale, I am really happy to be here.

I spend these two weeks very happily, the old routine returns, breakfast, a walk into Riva, or just a stroll along the lake, sunbathe and snooze for a while, with a dip in the pool. Around mid-afternoon, just when the sun is hot, I wander back to my room and invariably go to see Mario. Sometimes we go out into the mountains, or to a local lake, sometimes we stay in his room and listen to music.

Sometimes we spend the afternoons separately and I either read, go for a walk or go back to the pool. I enjoy this as it reminds me that I can still enjoy myself alone, I don't need someone else in order to be content.

Evenings, I still enjoy dressing for dinner and linger over getting ready, and eat my dinner slowly. People in the restaurant sometimes stop to talk to me, and the staff are now making a real fuss of me, pausing to chat.

This is a new phase in my journey. This is the first time I have returned anywhere, and become familiar with my surroundings and vice versa. It could have been a real disappointment, but it isn't. Another sigh of relief.

One night I am feeling very brave. I have brought a new dress with me. It is citrus green, backless with tiny shoestring straps, and a hem cut on a slash. It looks really good with my deep suntan, but is more noticeable than anything else I have worn at either hotel. This is definitely held up with will power!

The second trip I made to see Mario, he said to me one night when I was dressed up for dinner, "Gillian, you are very beautiful and very elegant, but it is this I am really interested in." He was pointing at his forehead. He meant my brain. This was very flattering, however I did feel a bit put out that I wasn't physically as beautiful as he found my brain!

By the end of this two week break, we have learned to communicate much better, but it is still far from perfect. I decide that I should try and learn a little of the Italian language to help things. Strangely, as time progresses, some of my really awful French returns to me, not very useful in Italy, but some of the words are similar and some of the verbs are almost identical. Trouble is I was hopeless at French at school!

Ah well, time will tell, que sera, sera!

I return to the autumn sunshine of England. It's lovely to be home. I've had a fantastic summer and discovered things about myself that I never knew before. The main thing of which is, it's not just o.k. to be alone, it's really good fun. Different, but fun! Along with freedom, self-reliance, and a bit of help from my friends, life is good...

ITALIAN

…Returning to work, I tell my friends about my holiday and how wonderful it was, before settling back into the old routine. Walking into the filing room is a new face.

'Who's that?' I ask someone.

'That's Lucio, he's our new casual. He's Italian!'

'Blimey, I can't believe it,' and I head off into the filing room.

'Hello, I'm Gill, I'm told you are Italian?'

'Yes'

'I want to learn Italian! Can you tell me the best way to learn?'

'Well my sister teaches at night school?'

'Great! When?'

'Tuesday evenings at the local College.'

'Oh, that's no good. I am at college on Tuesday evenings.'

'Well, I could always teach you.'

'That would be great, when and where?'

'Leave it with me and I'll let you know. I'll speak to my sister about it. To be honest I've never taught anyone before, but I start my PGCE in September, so it will be good practice for me. This job is a stop gap in between'

'Great, Thanks very much.'

A couple of days later, Lucio comes to see me. 'I've spoken to my sister and I've sorted out some ideas, so we just need to decide which day or days you want to do.'

We decide on Mondays and Thursdays after work.

COLLEGE

Having now got all the autumn and winter to look forward to and encouraged by the comments by the holiday rep, I decide to pursue the idea of learning to do body massage. I check the local colleges, and am trying to decide where to go.

Stourbridge don't do a course, and so Dudley is looking likely, trouble is, it's cold enough in Dudley in summer, it's very high up, and with not much to stop the icy blasts flying in from the Ural Mountains in Russia, in winter it's absolutely freezing.

Whilst pondering this, one Sunday afternoon I am visiting my Godmother in West Bromwich and tell her I am thinking about going to college, but don't fancy Dudley in winter. She gives me a copy of Sandwell College's prospectus and I see West Bromwich does a course in Body Massage. Great. I go home and next day call them. It's September and enrolment is starting. I get through and am told they only have one place available. I am at work and am worried that by the time I get there, it will have gone. I offer to pay over the phone to secure a place, but the lady tells me not to worry, if I can get there today, they will save me a place.

I leave work early and head off to West Bromwich. I find the desk and enrol. They tell me that I also have to study anatomy and physiology. It is on a Wednesday evening for three hours, 5.30 to 8.30.

Three weeks later and I am starting college! I haven't been to college since leaving school. Although I am looking forward to it, I am also nervous. What if I can't do it? What about all those new people? How will I get on with them? Only one way to find out!

I walk in through the college doors and find myself in the central hallway of a Victorian building. With a beautiful Minton tiled floor, I am directed upstairs to the classroom. As I climb the stairs, with its cast iron-work banister, now softened with numerous layers of paint, I am led up towards a beautiful stained

117

glass window. A few of the small panes have been broken, but otherwise nothing has really changed. I imagine the noise and chatter of the children's voices in what used to be the local grammar school, to which my mother attended in the 1930's.

I imagine her here as a young girl, and realise that this is the first time I have ever been in this building, despite living in West Bromwich throughout my childhood. During all the time I consequently spend here I always have a mind to times past. How many children have been educated within its walls, and now as an adult I am joining in. I wonder, did my mother sit in this room, I know she must have climbed the stairs numerous times.

I find it amazing how the present is dictated by the past. Set in stone, each decision made having a consequence that leads me to this place where my mother must have had all her hopes and dreams to look forward to. And now I am walking up the same stairs maybe putting my footstep over an exact place that she had trodden. If I need any guiding hand to help me over the next few months, I think I have come to the right place.

Walking into the classroom, there are a few people here already. The room has couches lining each of two opposing walls, with stools behind. I take a place at a vacant bed so I am sitting alone. Eventually there are around 30 people and then Kate, our tutor arrives.

I have to say that this first hour, is nothing short of chaos, and I am feeling slightly stressed by the end of it. I find it hard to believe that people haven't enrolled properly, and they are sent off to various places in the college to complete various tasks, while the rest of us sit and watch.

Eventually we are taught a little massage, and then we all go home! I assume it will be better next time...

...Yes, yes you're ahead of me. More chaos, but as the time passes, we settle down and I spend one hour a week studying anatomy and physiology, and two doing body massage.

During the first session I hear one lady mention that she is also studying reflexology. During our introductions she tells us she has twelve children! I decide during the evening that if she can do this with twelve children, then I have no excuse not to do the same! The more qualifications I have the better. I will try to enrol for this too. Other than knowing the principle of it, I know nothing else. Next day I revisit college after work and am accepted onto the course which is on Tuesday nights.

So, my weeks are suddenly filled with learning and studying. Mondays are 2 hours of Italian, Tuesday, 3 hours reflexology, Wednesday, 3 hours of A&P and body massage, Thursday, 2 hours of Italian, and Friday, I am off! Saturday's are homework, and on the seventh day, I wonder how I got myself into all this!

JANE-THE-MASSEUSE

During the first couple of weeks several people on the courses go on holiday, a few more drop out of the courses quite quickly, (I wonder why they go to all that trouble and then leave!) and it takes around a month before we are settled into 'the regulars!' On my massage course I find I have started working with a girl called Jane, and very soon we become really good friends. She has a fantastic sense of humour, which is even funnier when she goes into a panic over something.

During A&P we are required to learn all the different body systems. We are given lots of booklets to complete as a means of learning, and each week, we are given a quick tour of this particular body system and then sent home to complete our booklets with the help of our own recently purchased books on A&P.

The whole set have to be completed by the end of March. The tutorials are always a bit chaotic, as we are either distracted, someone has a problem to be sorted, someone still hasn't registered properly, (well there's a surprise!) or other innocuous reasons I can't remember. Jane and I become a little frustrated, and fearing an exam we won't have a clue about at the end, decide to meet up and do our booklets together.

Saturday mornings become our date at my house, as we drink tea, chat, put the world to rights, oh, and do some A&P! We do so well we finish our books by the end of January, and spend the rest of the term much more relaxed and without any pressure. The lessons are then treated by us as a way of refreshing our new found knowledge, or whispering quietly about anything and everything.

The one thing that I am looking forward to on my course, which really fascinates me, is how a group of individuals, who have never met before, interact with one another. Our massage group is great and after several weeks, we all really get on well together.

Within minutes of arriving on the first evening, I have scanned the room and made a quick assumption of how the land lies. No doubt all this is not unique to me, but I am really keen to try and see how the group develops. Who is going to lead, who will struggle, who will be the most studious, and so on. I am also interested in how I will fit into this group.

Apart from being on holiday, when up to a point I was playing a part, this is the first time in many, many years, I am with a group of people who don't know me, and whom I do not know. I want to know what they will think of me. How will they judge me? At work you develop a reputation for this or that. With your friends you are seen as this or that, and most of the time one new situation is entwined with another. People know you as 'so and so's' sister, friend, work mate, etc. We are invariably met by a prejudgment of some description and so you never really get judged as a blank specimen. Neither do we tend to find ourselves on an equal footing, where we all start from the same place. Even when I have attended courses from work, although often we don't know each other, we have all come from the same work background, and are there for the same reason. On this course, it's different. We have all come from different places, we all do different things, and I am intrigued to know what has brought us all here together just now. Whose lives are happy, who is in turmoil, what on earth made you decide to do a course in body massage. It is endless, and I am not disappointed, but I am surprised!

To say that starting learning again after twenty odd years is a shock to my system is a bit of an understatement. Although work is constantly changing, new rules, change for change sake, essentially it's more of the same, and it evolves.

Here and at home, I am learning completely different things. Brand new subjects, and all at the same time. How mad am I? Still I suppose I am running true to form. In head first again, gasp for breath as the water is deeper than I thought. However, it feels wonderful to be doing something different and I wonder all the time where this path will lead me.

During the A&P I seem always to be the one asking questions, and I think that everyone else must understand it, and I am the thickie! Even when it is explained to me, I don't always get it. I ask until I understand, and now and again, someone else asks a question. The thing that really amazes me is that over time, people then start to ask me to explain to them! I am seen as one of the clever ones! It takes me a while to work this out, but it seems that asking questions is seen as clever.

This doesn't always apply, as my Italian lessons will prove, when asking questions is really confusing, since I don't understand the answers!

On the whole I really start to enjoy college, I like the group of people I am with, and we always have fun together, swapping stories as we dip into each others' lives, although the journey to West Bromwich during rush hour becomes a bit tedious. The worst of this is one evening when a local factory catches fire and gridlock happens.

West Bromwich now sits in the middle of the motorway network. They say it has the busiest motorway junction in Europe, I would not disagree, and so slow traffic is a daily grind. However, if there is an accident, or it gets really snarled up, the traffic leaves the motorway and takes to the roads to move up a few junctions. This particular night, there was an accident on the motorway, and a fire in West Bromwich. Chaos supreme!! No-one went anywhere, and the knock on effect radiated out to Dudley and Wolverhampton, and all places in between. My sister took three hours to get home on a normally forty minute journey, and I got my timing wrong and took one and a half hours to travel half a mile! Some of the students never made it at all.

Other than the traffic, there are a few minor things that irritate me as the course progresses, one of which is that there is never enough couch roll, and another is that there are never enough towels, and so each week is a stressful battle to secure these two items in order to complete our tasks.

Another thing that really starts to annoy me is the standard of the printed pictures on the handouts, which I am then expected to label and learn, never mind the possibility that they may ask me to draw one in an exam! One evening I really lose my rag as the overhead projector screen can't be found. I am dumbstruck as one of the patterned curtain privacy screens is pulled across and used as a foil by which to study the heart! I blow a fuse, complaining that I am paying for this course and I expect to have the right tools and equipment by which to study! It doesn't make much difference, but I feel better for complaining.

Having said that our tutor is great, a really lovely lady, who hasn't a bad bone in her body. She is a wonderful masseuse, and we get on really well together. It transpires we have things in common...

Over the duration of the course, we all get to know each other, including our tutor Kate. Towards the end of the course Kate, myself and another girl decide to do a Reiki course, I am already aware that Kate lives near me, and she says she will drive. I give her my address, and she says 'Oh, I know roughly where that is, I used to do some beauty treatment for a lady up that way. As I give her more specific directions as to which road, and which house, she says, that's Mrs Ellis's house!

'Yes!' I reply.

'I used to do her beauty treatments!'

'Heaven's, what a coincidence, I bought her bungalow after she died! What did you think of her?'

'She was quite a character. Very precise, a bit intimidating to be honest. I used to have to dye her eyebrows for her, and she wouldn't have the whole lot done, I had to dye only each individual hair that was white. It used to take me ages!'

'I'm not surprised, I never met her but I believe she was quite a character. You know she set up the spiritualist church in Stourbridge?'

'No, you're joking, I never knew that!

'It's true.'

'I've been there. I never knew it was anything to do with her!'

'Well she was a spiritualist. Apparently, she and her late husband set it up. Did she ever tell you anything?'

'I never knew she was a spiritualist, she never said a word. I'm absolutely amazed!'

We chatted on for a while discussing the gossip that I had heard about her, and I told her about how when I was decorating, I was always aware of a presence, and used to wonder whether she liked and approved of the changes I made to her home. At the time I had no idea of her reputation as a spiritualist.

At the end of the college year, we prepare for our exams. As Jane-the-Masseuse goes into a meltdown of panic we do some studying together. We have been told what the questions will be on, so just need to learn the answers. Sounds easy, and it isn't as bad as we thought, except that as it is another new brain activity not practised for the last twenty-odd years, it is quite challenging and daunting. As we all sit down and settle into answering the questions the room falls silent.

Towards the end of the exam, our tutor leaves the room for a few minutes. Within seconds, one of the girls turns to me and asks me 'What's the answer to the last question? We weren't told to revise that.'

Just as I begin to answer, someone else says, 'Speak up, I can't hear you!'

I realise then that everyone is looking to me for the answer! I tell them all what I believe to be the answer, emphasising that it is only my opinion, and I may be wrong.

'Of course you will be right, you know everything!' someone says.

'What do you mean?' I ask.

'Well, you're the clever one of the group'

'No I'm not! Why do you say that?'

'Because you are! You ask all the questions and understand everything.'

'But that's because I don't understand and I want to know!'

'Yes but you ask the questions, and then explain it to us so that we understand! The rest of us are too frightened to ask because we haven't got a clue!'

Almost lost for words, I answer the question. The room goes quiet again and our tutor returns. I realise then the answer to my original question about the group.

Generally, they have all seen me as the clever one, and a leader. I am genuinely surprised, as I never saw myself as that. From my perspective, whenever I didn't understand anything I asked and asked until I did. I was always thinking that I was the thickie because the others just seemed to be getting on with it.

There is, however, one notable exception to this. 'The Blue Books!' These are designed to prove underpinning knowledge to the examiners. Heaven knows who designed them, but they prove to be more difficult to fill in than learning the contents of the course! Eventually though after lots of hours tugging at our tutor's sleeve, we all manage to get the books completed.

And all of a sudden, there it is. The end of a full academic year and those of us who completed the course have all passed. We just have to wait for the certificates to arrive. Time has slipped by so quickly. We have all made some new friends and look forward to a summer of nothing much to do other than work and a holiday or two!

MORE ITALIAN

To be honest, although I love English language and words, I was never very good at foreign languages at school. I wasn't really interested in them, and in my schooldays during the '70's I couldn't really see the point in learning French or German since there was no way I would get the opportunity to use it. We didn't travel abroad and the idea of working abroad would never have crossed my mind. It didn't help that both language teachers weren't that wonderful or inspiring. My French teacher spent most of the two years we were studying 'O' levels off sick. We degenerated from an 'O' level group to a pretty poor CSE group. I got a grade 3 CSE and was amazed to have achieved so well!

My mother was very grammatically correct and spent years correcting our English, so although I know how to write and speak properly, (except for my black-country accent) we were never taught the rules of language at school. I know the basics of a verb and a noun, and the past and present tenses, but ask me about pluperfect or past historic, and it really does become foreign language!

So, you can sort of get the idea that Lucio is in for a struggle...!

The one thing that I have going for me is enthusiasm and a real interest in my subject. After that there is not a lot else!

We start with the basics:

'My name is Gillian, my age is 38, I live in England, how are you? I am well thank you. The book is on the table.'

What? The book is on the table? Why do I want to learn that? Well, it seems that whatever language you learn, you have to learn 'the book is in the table!' Comes as standard in the language books!

Right!

After that, we struggle! But with my new enthusiasm for learning, my homework is to learn the present tense of two verbs. Same as other languages the verbs 'to be,' and 'to have.' Both irregular of course just to whet my appetite!

I go home, and stop off at Jane's on the way. I tell her of my new skill and then start wondering how on earth I am to learn these verbs.

Jane speaks French, and within a few minutes knows the Italian verbs I am to learn, because they are so similar in French. This makes me feel worse, but I resolve to go and learn them for next lesson.

I fail!

Still positive though I comfort myself that I still know more than I did last week, so that's good, yes?

Next lesson, we learn to count. Marvellous! I go home, and later that evening I tell Mario on the telephone, I have learned to count.

Well actually, I thought I'd said I am learning to count, but as if to reinforce my need to learn Italian, I got it wrong.

Too late and too hard to try and explain, Mario asks me enthusiastically to count to twenty. Eager to retain a bit of dignity, I grab my dictionary and recite the numbers. Carried away with enthusiasm, I don't notice that the numbers also show, multiples of tens, hundreds, thousands up to a million!

'Gillian, that is marvellous, you can count to a million! You have learned all that today. You will soon be fluent in Italian!'

Wrong! But I don't let on.

After a few weeks we decide that we can squeeze in some extra lessons occasionally and so some Saturday mornings when I am not doing other lots of homework we have an extra lesson. Eventually, I start to pick things up and also discover that my best way of learning is by repetition. Six times to be exact. So if I am learning items in the kitchen, Lucio tells me the list of items, then points at them and I repeat back. By the sixth attempt I usually remember the whole lot.

If only it was as easy with the grammar! I become quite adept at reciting verbs but all those little words in between to make up the sentences, and in the correct tense have Lucio rushing to the oven to shove his head in!

Every now and then I show flashes of brilliance and we are both amazed. Especially when it's often the complicated things I get the grasp of, but the simple things elude me.

One such example is when he teaches me to tell the time. I am absolutely hopeless!

We spend weeks coming back to it in between other things, each time I am still hopeless! Eventually, I am the one saying 'can we do the time?'

Lucio puts his head in his hands despairingly and says 'Noooo, not the time, please, I can't!'

Then with a flash of my childhood crossing my mind, I have a deja-vu. (Gosh a bit of French there!) When I was a child, my mother started to teach me how to tell the time. I remember vividly, sitting on her knee with a wooden jigsaw clock, which had a picture of a cockerel on it, (As I type this, I have only just realised the significance of the cockerel!) repeating after my mother, 'o'clock, quarter-past, half-past, quarter-to.'

But it meant nothing to me and I failed miserably!

I also remember distinctly, a lesson at primary school. "Children you are going to be taught the 24 hour clock today..."

Ahead of me again, you can imagine can't you? What did make an impression though was that the teacher told us that they use a 24hour clock at railway stations. I think that helped confuse me even more. She had an example of one of these clocks, and I think I thought that when you went to a railway station they told the time differently, but that it only happened in railway stations. Then I started to worry that I would get stuck if I ever went unaccompanied to a railway station, since I wouldn't be able to tell the time either to catch a train or find my way off the platform. And I am only eight or nine years old!

Eventually though, it got through and I am not aware of any lasting scars... until now!

Exactly the same things that I struggled with as a child happen again. Filled with my "Pollyanna" optimism of "things to be glad about" I reason that I am glad to have discovered something seemingly fundamental about the way my brain works, or more precisely, doesn't work, in that the difficulty I have is not bound by language, so therefore it must be the principal of telling the time that I struggle with.

The ironic thing is, in my now adult life, I really like clocks! I also like sundials and weather veins and remember something else my mother taught me, the principle of 'local time.'

If you are too young to have heard of local time, it means that the sun reaches its highest point at midday. As the earth turns, the sun reaches its highest point at different places at different times. Years ago, towns set their clocks to midday at the time when the sun reached its highest point. The confusing thing was that the train timetables also ran to local time. Can you imagine how confusing that would be nowadays? You could probably be a time-traveller as your Virgin super-fast tilting train leaves Birmingham and arrives in Oxford before you left home! Great if you're late for work though!

Anyway back to Italian. As you can imagine, one day, quite unexpectedly and, with no apparent explanation, in a similar way as happened in 'My Fair Lady' "She got it!" Or rather I got it! I could tell the time, in English and Italian. This must be one of my finest achievements.

Lucio can't believe his luck!

Every now and again we have a break. Usually because I am going back to Italy for a few days.

We spend each lesson before I travel practicing speaking, asking questions, 'What time is the train to Rovereto? How much is a ticket to Rovereto? Can I have the bill please? The book is on the table'. Damn! Slipped in again!

Brimming with my new found confidence one day, I leave work, go to college, go home, have a few hours' kip, before setting off for the airport in the middle of the night.

I learn another world exists in these hours. An army of technicians, maintenance engineers, cleaners and cone dropper/collectors appear like an army of ants to maintain our motorway network. I find travelling at this time very relaxing and feel very safe. Mainly it's just lorries and me travelling. Rarely is there a need for lorries to change lanes, they glide gently and quietly along. Everyone seems calm and relaxed and there are only a few cars out and about.

I park my car, take the bus to the terminal building and before I know it I am eating my obligatory tuna mayonnaise sub-roll courtesy of Ryanair. Quick snooze afterwards and we are descending into the familiar airport at Brescia. It's time to get my thinking cap on and practice my new skills.

Ryanair have a bus that goes from the airport to Verona central station. After I collect my case I go through to arrivals and after withdrawing some cash, I walk into the bus ticket-office.

In my best Italian I ask 'Can I have a ticket to Verona please?'

'Blahdeblahdeblah-o' comes the reply from the clerk who is looking at me expectantly.

Shit! I suddenly discover a flaw in my plan. I can't understand a word they say back to me!

Mumbling in my disgruntled English I ask again and am given my ticket.

Hmm! Back to the drawing board, or more correctly, white board, I need to refine my listening skills.

The funny thing is I suddenly find myself thinking in French! French of all things. I was crap at it at school and now I keep finding bits of it interrupting me when I least expect it! "Must try harder" as the teachers love to tell us so easily. Well, twenty something years later, I may be ready to retake my exam again.

Feeling a bit better after a few days, I decide to buy a newspaper and magazine to practice my reading skills. At least I haven't got to engage in conversation so feel safe again.

Wrong again! Because I am buying Italian language goodies, the newsagent assumes I am a linguistic genius and chatters away to me in Italian! I smile and laugh as though I understand every word and hand over a large note to cover the cost. As I walk away I manage a cheery Italian goodbye and make a hasty exit before I can engage in any further conversation.

Back home I use them with Lucio to practice translation. Often completely off key, but slowly I improve. I practice my verbs and spend hours reading the dictionary learning words and drop off to sleep at night talking to myself in Italian.

Learning the skill of engaging in a two way conversation becomes almost as arduous as learning to tell the time. I eventually develop a knack for talking with Lucio, but when he plays me a tape and asks me questions on it I am hopelessly lost again.

However, slowly and surely I make progress. I learn new tenses, my translation gets better and my writing improves. Sometimes having a few weeks off proves to be a good idea. When we start again, Lucio's brow furrows as he tests my knowledge to see what I can remember, and it's amazing. Things seem to have stuck and I remember amazingly well! He is astounded. Well we both are!

After a couple of years, yes years, I become more fluent. I find I am able to follow conversation, laughing in the right places, and am able to ask for directions, go shopping, and eventually have a conversation with Mario's mother.

She doesn't speak one word of English, and on past meetings she chatters away to me like a long lost friend and I haven't a clue what she is saying.

One day we go to see her, and at last, I can understand her and more importantly, she can understand me!

This is really wonderful. The thing is with language, you can't blag it. If you can't speak it properly, you won't be understood. It's as simple as that. Moreover, you cannot engage in a conversation.

I feel that at long last, I have climbed a barrier to another world. Mario and I speak a mixture of both languages, but when he chatters away in Italian, I can respond.

Then one morning I wake up and realise that I have been dreaming in Italian language. They say that when you dream in a foreign language, you have cracked it! I'm not sure if that's true, but I feel really happy about it!

A NEW WINTER

The end of this glorious summer inevitably comes to an end. I have gone through a metamorphosis that Shirley Valentine would be proud of. I have learned so much. So many things about myself that I never knew. So many things about myself that my friends and family never knew either. I feel I am being treated with a new form of respect.

Generally, I feel that I can be relied upon to get myself in a pickle and entertain everyone who sits waiting to say "Well, I saw it coming, but you do have to find out for yourself don't you. Let's put the kettle on and you can be refreshed ready for your next disaster!"

But this time they are saying, "Come in, put the kettle on, tell us about your latest adventure!" Maybe I am becoming a mature grown-up woman after all!

Like many others the hotel closes around the end of October for the winter. I go over for a few days in the final week. Quiet and tranquil, with just a few guests, it seems it's time to hibernate. The cool autumn air refreshingly fills my lungs as I walk along the lake into Riva. The trees are changing to the reds and golds and that lovely October clear watery sunshine is everywhere. Optimism says that it is just a brief moment of well deserved sleep for all before the new spring bursts into life again.

Mario tells me he has a month off before starting his winter job in St. Moritz in Switzerland. He asks me if I would like to go to visit him there during the winter.

St Moritz? The playground of the rich and famous? Lots of snow and the Cresta run? Err... Oh go on then!

In between we arrange for him and his friend to come and visit me in England for a few days. Neither of them have ever been out of London so would love to see a different side of England.

With a little help from Jacqueline and Jane, I tidy the house, do a bit of life laundry, and await my guests.

Travelling to the airport in my little metro, I hope they haven't brought too much luggage!

Feeling a little nervous, I wait at arrivals. They emerge shortly after and we greet one another as old friends.

Squeezing into my car we set off around the M25 and out of London we head off north along the M40.

There's a particular place along the M40 that I love. You come up a long hill and under a big high bridge through a cutting, and just at the top of the rise, there is one of the most glorious views of England. It represents everything I imagine foreign visitors find wonderful about our country. It has an unrestricted vista across towards Gloucester to the west and all the way across towards the Vale of the White Horse to the east. I find it easy to see why this area has such a spiritual connection. It fills me with glory and optimism every time I travel there. Because it is so low lying, there is often a veil of mist covering it, so you can never be guaranteed to see it. This adds to the sense of wonder and excitement for me, and stops me taking it for granted, like a jewel that sparkles more brightly in the bright sunshine.

We travel companionably chatting away, but then I suddenly notice they have both gone very quiet.

'Are you o.k.?' I ask.

'Yes fine'

'You're very quiet, everything all right?'

'Gillian, where are all the houses?'

'Pardon?'

'Where are all the houses? In London there are houses everywhere. I thought it was like that everywhere in England. There are no houses, just fields and green. It's beautiful.'

'Yes, it is, isn't it' I reply. 'London is like any capital city. The rest of the country is different.'

We spend the next few days going out and about, meeting my friends and family, and eating and drinking. The three of us get on well together and they both love the area in which I live. Nothing too dramatic, but we all have a sense of where we all live and who we are that gives us a better understanding of one another's lives.

Before we know it we are waving goodbye to each other as they pass through departures, and I am returning to the peace and tranquillity of home.

I enjoy their company, but having lived alone for some time, I enjoy my own company and order. It's hard work having to entertain and make decisions!

ST. MORITZ

Winter arrives and I take the plunge and arrange to travel to St. Moritz. A new adventure and a new journey to undertake.

The journey involves travelling to Birmingham airport, so that's good because it's near home. Then fly to Zurich, then a train to Chur, and then change to go to St. Moritz. Quite a long way, but I look forward to the challenge!

The flight is fine, I am used to that now, and the train station at Zurich is underneath the airport so that's easy. I discover that Zurich main station is huge, but easy to navigate, so before I know it I am watching the Swiss countryside flying past.

Eventually, the train arrives at Chur and we disembark. A little old-fashioned looking train is on the next track and the announcer declares that this is "the fast train to St. Moritz." Lovely, that means I should be there in no time!

Wrong again! It chugs and crawls its way through the mountains twisting and winding seemingly always upwards, over high bridges and through long tunnels, rocking and shaking as the wheels squeal along the bendy tracks. The plus side though is that the scenery is spectacularly beautiful and this makes the journey pass by a lot more quickly. I believe some people travel on this train purely for the beauty of the scenery and I can understand why.

Eventually I arrive at St. Moritz station and am met by lots and lots of snowy mountains, and a frozen lake. Very beautiful, but very cold!

Mario is waiting for me and after a hug takes me to the hotel he is working in.

There is really only one hotel to stay in at St. Moritz, and this is the one where he works. He lives in the staff quarters which are reached through a side door which leads to a series of underground tunnels, stairs, lifts and eventually staff quarters on several floors. His room is spacious and has a window that looks across to the town. Very comfortable.

Although he is working split shifts, we go out and about in between and when he is working during the day I wander the streets of St. Moritz. I have to say that I am very unimpressed by this! Full of designer shops, but although this is no different to other places, here, the staff look at you over their designer glasses or under their surgically altered noses. (That's not strictly true, since most of the shops are staffed by local people, but that is how they make me feel.) The other thing is that at around three o'clock in the afternoon, the sun goes down and in the space of a few minutes, it is absolutely freezing cold! Even with warm gloves and a really 'non P.C' wool and angora coat that has an even more 'non P.C' big fur collar, it's really, really cold! Lots of the shops sell fur coats, and to be honest, and very controversially, I can see why. Fur really does keep you warm, and in these temperatures (minus 20 and below) being cold is a serious issue. Hurtling down mountains on ski's keeps you warm. Walking around sedately doesn't!

So, invariably when the sun goes down, I return to the warmth of the hotel and read, relax or have a snooze. I find I have very little energy, and my nose bleeds from time to time, so I think the altitude and cold affects me quite a lot.

When Mario is free, he takes me out. We go out to eat, travel around a little bit and one day he takes me up a mountain.

Blimey! I thought it was cold in St. Moritz, but up this mountain feels arctic to me! The cold penetrates in minutes and I have to retreat indoors. The thermometer outside reads minus 28 degrees! After a warm drink, we return down the mountain to the almost balmy temperature of minus 18! A quick stop for a warming mug of Gluwein and I start to thaw. I hope you are getting the picture that I don't enjoy being cold!

After a few days I am back at the station waiting for the "fast train to Chur" and my journey home. Reflecting on my new experience, I have enjoyed myself, but don't enjoy the atmosphere of this trendy designer town in winter. I am sure in spring and summer when the snow and skiers have gone away to their summer haunts St. Moritz is much more like Heidi-land, with spring and summer flowers dominating the lush green mountainsides and crystal clear mountain streams leading down to the lakes. In winter they shroud themselves in snow to keep their natural beauty secrets away from the undeserving superficial-dom that expends excess in the designer-wear winter shops.

Travelling on the train and the man in front of me speaks to me in German. I respond in Italian and after a fraught few minutes I remember I am English! I ask him if he speaks English, which he does and we pass a pleasant hour chatting before he leaves the train. I laugh to myself for being so intent on learning Italian I actually forgot I am English!

As for Mario and me, we have now evolved into a brotherly-sisterly friendship that is undemanding and companionable. Good friends that enjoy one another's company and then return to our own world. I travel again to St. Moritz once more this winter and then before I know it summer is nearly here again!

As time progresses, I realise just how much I enjoy the freedom of my home and that this other little world that I have created is one which I can step into and out of whenever I want to. I am not answerable to anyone and with no responsibility I realise after a while that for the first time in my life that I can remember, I feel that I am in control. I can do more or less what I want, when I want and with whom I want. I feel grown up! This other little world of my own which is well away from home cannot be influenced by anyone apart from me and those in it and if I start to find I don't like it I can abandon it which means that home becomes a real inner sanctum for me that is safe, warm and comfortable.

I reflect on my past year or so. I have done things I would never have imagined, I have made lots of new friends, gone to college, have passed exams that mean I am qualified in anatomy & physiology, reflexology and Swedish body massage and I have started to learn a new language. I feel quite pleased with myself!

A WINTER TRIP TO RIVA

In between winter and summer they hold an international shoe fair in Riva. Mario returns from St. Moritz for the event and I go over to spend a few days there.

Generally, although Riva del Garda is a very old town, and there are residents who live their lives in and around there, during the winter lots of people migrate. Many in the tourist industry go back to families, whilst others go to spend the winter in the snowy winter resorts elsewhere. Riva really only comes to life properly in the summer.

The hotel I normally stay in is full, having been taken over by "the shoe people." No matter, I stay in a lovely hotel next door although they only do bed and breakfast. In the evenings if Mario is working I go out to one of the local bars or restaurants to eat and practise my slowly improving Italian. I discover a new problem. I speak to them in my best Italian, and they start to reply in something I really don't understand. I ask them to repeat slowly, and they repeat it again and then ask me if I am German!

How frustrating. I have spent months learning to speak Italian and people are responding to me in German! I start to wonder whether I should stick to English, at least we all know where we stand then. However I persist and after a time I learn to recognise when they respond in German and politely say (in Italian) I am English.

Many months later my accent must improve and people respond in Italian to me and this becomes another milestone for me! Anyway, eventually I am served my food and feel pleased that I am becoming more confident with my ability to speak.

The few days I spend here are lovely. Clear crisp blue skies, the sun shining and the lake brimming with excitement as the snowy mountains discharge their purified melt water into the rocky streams that feed new life into the lake. Only a few shops are open in the old town and it feels quiet and tranquil as I wander its streets.

The one thing that never eludes me in this place though is my ability to get completely lost within its narrow streets! Why this is, I have no idea! I recognise all the shops and the streets they are contained in. I just don't possess a mental map of how they all fit together which has a two-fold effect. If I am wandering aimlessly about every time I turn a corner there is a surprise waiting for me. However, if I am trying to find somewhere particular it becomes an even bigger surprise if I find it or a complete frustration if I don't and spend ages hunting for it. I am sure that as I walk, someone moves all the streets around for a joke.

I return to England again and look forward to a new summer.

A SECOND SUMMER

The second summer I spend building upon the first. Travelling back and forth on a regular basis to Riva has become second nature to me. I am on one such trip when I realise how easy and familiar it has all become. I am so engrossed in my book that I haven't noticed we have gone hurtling down the runway and we are up in the air before I realise it. I remember so clearly what seems like a lifetime ago that first flight on my own and being so anxious about what lay ahead. How things change!

I have become comfortable in my now familiar surroundings and have met several new people thanks to Mario's network of friends and acquaintances.

One evening we go to meet some new people. I am not sure they will speak English, and have got lots of Italian words flying around my head ready to unleash should the opportunity arise. I have tried this several times already and whilst my enthusiasm is well received, the ability to get all the words in the right order is still something of a mystery. This particular evening, everyone is chattering away in Italian and I am listening hard when one of the girls starts talking to me in English. Her English is marvellous and I ask her where she learnt to be so fluent. She tells me she and her brother run a green-grocers in Riva and for many years an English lady used to stay at a hotel in the town and began drinking coffee at a bar next to their shop. They became firm friends and the lady has become something of a mother figure to her now.

She asks me where I live in England and I tell her, south of Birmingham.

So does this lady.

'Where about?' I ask.

'Halesowen.' she replies.

'Gosh, that's the next town from where I live, around six miles away!'

145

We chat a while and she tells me where their shop is. 'Come in and see us anytime you are passing.'

'I will.' I reply.

Next day I take my walk into Riva after breakfast as normal and find myself outside her shop. She is there with her brother and introduces me to him.

She takes me next door for a coffee and we chat for a while before we go our separate ways. Over a period of time I call to see them often.

Strangely, I only ever see her twice, and develop a friendship with her brother. He also has a huge love of the English language and says he suffers wanderlust. Over a period of time I watch the shop evolve as fine wines, delicatessen items and the sound of classical music mixes with the cacophony of fruit and vegetables.

Mario knows neither the girl or her brother and I feel really happy that I have made an acquaintance or two of my own.

One visit I make and he asks me if I could obtain an English dictionary of etymology. He has been unable to find a decent one in Italy. I take one with me on my next trip to which he is very appreciative. This is of course before the advent of E-books, Amazon and E-bay!

I also get to see more of Mario's good friend Angelo who joins me for dinner occasionally, and the three of us go out in the evenings sometimes after work.

One evening Mario tells me we are all going for a drink after he finishes work. I am wearing a pair of white trousers, strapless bustier and a pair of silk Escada mules.

I make my way down to the car park and the boys are waiting for me. Angelo takes one look at me and starts to laugh. Mario leans forward and looks aghast.

'Gillian, why are you dressed like this?'

'What's wrong with it?' I ask a bit put out.

'Well it is too much dressed-up for fishing.'

'Fishing? What do you mean?'

146

'We are going fishing.' He says, as though it is the most normal thing to do at eleven o'clock at night in the middle of Riva.

'You never told me we were going fishing.' I reply

'Of course I did.'

'Mario, I can assure you, you did not tell me we were going fishing. I may be English but I am not eccentric enough to dress like this to go fishing! Let me go and change.'

'No we haven't time. Get in the car, you'll be fine!'

'But my white trousers and silk shoes?'

'You'll be fine. Come on let's go.'

So there we are. Me dressed to kill, and they dressed to fish. We drive a short distance and start to walk towards the lake. Unfortunately for me, the grass is being watered by an oscillator and I have to run the gauntlet to miss getting soaked. Added to which I am trying to avoid the puddles that have formed, to keep my shoes dry, all by the light of a not so silvery moon! Once settled, I get a blanket to sit on, a glass of wine and some nibbles. Half an hour goes by and all seems to be going well and I start to relax a little and then "Bang!" Blinding flash that lights up the lake like a stadium, followed by a nasty rumbling crash. The ground shakes and the heavens open. Thunder and lightning!

We pack up almost as quickly as the lightning flash and make a run for it. Priorities changes as the oscillator is forgotten and we dash to the car. We head off for a bar and I surreptitiously inspect my lovely shoes for damage. Amazingly they seem unscathed. Just a little damp and by morning they look perfect again. I am very relieved!

This incident however seems to have cemented me more into the affection of the boys and by the end of the evening I have been invited to dinner at Angelo's home that he shares with his parents for the most famous local regional dish of "ucellini." Little birds!

For the faint hearted look away now...

Apparently, this involves Angelo going out early in the morning shooting the "little birds" which are then deep fried in butter and served.

'Mmm... I can't wait! Unfortunately, I am sure I am busy that night, when is it?' I say.

'No, no it is lovely, a real delicacy.'

Eventually, I am persuaded to try it, but with a promise that if I hate it they won't be offended. I manage to avoid it for several months!

Later on during the year and one evening Mario, his friend who came to England with him, and I are invited to the home of one of the receptionists. We arrive and a few other people are already there. We sit in her garden chatting and sharing food and drinks. At some point during the conversation someone says something really funny. Slightly ahead of the game I burst out laughing. Everyone stops and stares at me. Oh damn, I think I've got it wrong.

'Sorry have I done something wrong?' I ask.

'No, you understand what is being said,' someone says.

A round of applause and toast ensues as I am welcomed into the group. 'You are truly one of us now!' (Maybe this means I get to avoid the "Uccellini?")

INDIAN HEAD MASSAGE

The end of another summer arrives again and at college a new academic year dawns. With our new found skill at massage and expertise in anatomy and physiology, Jane-the-Masseuse and I discuss the possibilities for a new course to see us through the winter. We decide on Indian Head Massage. It's only a short course and now we have the basics we think it should be easier. Well, it may be easier, but neither of really believe it could be any more chaotic. How wrong could we be!

It all starts well enough, we meet on the first evening and our tutor tells us that we have a lot to get through in a short space of time so we need to get cracking. We watch intently as she demonstrates the various moves and we then practice on each other. So far so good.

Next week, filled with optimism, we meet again. Just as we get going we are expelled from our lovely big room by a group that have already booked it! We are relegated to a small classroom, full of chairs and tables which becomes an assault course for gymnasts as we try and scramble our way in. We manage to get through the lesson and hope by next week things will be sorted.

Hey-ho no-way José! We are still stuffed into a classroom that seems to have become a furniture store, and we spend the next few weeks lessons uncomfortable, unplanned and uncontrolled. There is a group of young girls in our class that have been doing a beauty course together and they all know each other, but don't seem too keen to do as they are told. They talk all the time, and the tutor seems unable to make them shut up and listen. Often she seems to issue instructions but her words dissolve into the noise that is created from these other students. The class descends into chaos and I feel that the only way to find out what we are supposed to be doing is by asking the tutor one-to-one.

Thankfully, the course is short and we manage to get through it reasonably unscathed. Our assignments are completed and we even manage to fill in the dreaded blue books, all before the whistle blows for the end of the course. Another certificate to add to the collection, but the blood sweat and tears are clearly visible!

A SECOND WINTER
BACK TO ST MORITZ 2002

By the end of the second summer, Mario has a new girlfriend, Andrea. He has told her all about me and she is quite happy for us all to be friends.

The first conversation I have with her is in the middle of the night. There has been a 'misunderstanding' between Mario and her and things have got a bit out of hand. The UN peacekeepers were busy so I get the call. Mario and Andrea have had a row. Lots of sparks flying and voices raised as they compete to insist on who is right and wrong.

I have a chat with Mario and then speak to Andrea.

Andrea is German, widowed and she has two children. She has a great sense of humour, very quick-witted and wants to have fun. Mario is Italian, jealous of her having fun without him and doesn't share the same sense of humour she has. Explosive mix!

We chat for a time, she cries and I tell her not to worry, he's just being temperamental and will get over it in no time. I tell Mario, Andrea is just having fun and not to be so jealous. He asks me if I like her. I tell him that she seems lovely but between tears in the middle of the night probably isn't the best way to get to know her!

On another of my trips to Riva, they have another telephone row and I mediate again. Peace reigns for a time and everything seems fine. Winter arrives and Andrea invites me to stay in her home from Boxing Day until the New Year. By now we have talked often on the phone together. We are just a few days apart in age, and share a similar humour. Her English is wonderful, (what a relief since learning Italian has been tortuous!) since she worked on an American army base as a translator for a time.

The plan is that I go to her home for a couple of days, and then we drive down to St. Moritz for New

151

Year. Her children are to stay with her mum so we can have a bit of fun together.

We spend a wonderful time in her home, her friends all arrive and we have a fondue, lots of bubbly and sing around her grand piano. Lovely!

Next thing we are packed and off to St. Moritz. She has a convertible top of the range Mercedes and is a very competent driver. I sit and relax watching the German countryside pass by my window. Eventually we are at the bottom of the Bernina Pass in Switzerland surrounded by lots of snow. All sorts of vehicles are crawling up the windy pass, higher and higher. Thankfully Andrea is completely relaxed and we slowly and steadily pass lots of 4x4 vehicles stranded or sliding along the pass.

Eventually we reach the top and slowly descend into St.Moritz. We unpack the car and once settled, enjoy a well-deserved drink!

Mario has switched hotels this year. There is a new Kempinski hotel and lots of the waiters have moved here. The accommodation Mario has is small but very comfortable. A bit of a squeeze but we all manage to fit in. The accommodation for the other waiters we 'unlovingly' call 'The Container!'

It is a sort of prefabricated tin shack. Apparently, the hotel intends to make some proper accommodation but for the time being there are lots of people sharing 'The Container.' Very basic accommodation, flimsy dividing walls, shared facilities, but it is at least warm and dry! Some of the waiters from Riva are working and staying here so it all feels nice and homely.

I am invited to stay in the container as there is a spare bed which gives us all a bit of breathing space.

We get off to a flying start. We go out to eat, have a few drinks, chat into the early hours as people drop in to say hello. Next day and whilst Mario works, Andrea decides to go skiing. As she ski's, I read a book and drink hot chocolate in the bar.

Later we eat and drink together as Mario is working late. When he finishes work, he comes back with more friends and we have an impromptu party.

Before we know it, it's New Year's Eve and we are standing watching the most spectacular firework display I can ever remember seeing. There is a big ski competition taking place at the time and money is no object as the competitors and sponsors are entertained.

Very late, I return to the container with some of the others and we are all asleep in no time.

A couple of days later and Mario tells us he is finishing work around 4.00pm. Andrea and I decide to take a walk to the Segantini museum just up the hill from the town centre. We spend an hour or so looking around before wandering back into the town. The sun is starting to go down and we decide to stop off for a Gluwein to warm us up.

Wrapped up against the cold we go to an outside bar in the centre of town. The bar is on a raised wooden platform and there are three steps up to it. Being on a platform, patio heaters lit and with a warm mug of Gluwein in our hands we soon feel quite snug.

This is only the second time I have had Gluwein and I really enjoy it. Andrea buys the first drink and I buy the second. Whilst we are chatting a young man starts to talk to us, and then insists on buying us a drink. Andrea then feels obliged to buy another round which then leaves the next round for me. Time is ticking on but we are having a nice time and feeling a rosy glow thanks to the warm Gluwein and our new friend insists we have one more Gluwein before we leave.

All of a sudden I feel very tired. Unaware that Gluwein has lots of alcohol in it, I have no idea that I am getting rather drunk. Naïve, I now know, but at the time I believed that because Gluwein is hot, any alcohol in it evaporates like it does when you are cooking with alcohol. Wrong, wrong, wrong!

So, feeling tired I put my mug down on the bar, and with my hands in my pockets decide I need to relax a little. With no chairs or stools to sit on, the young man we are drinking with is, I believe, standing right behind me and I decide he won't mind if I lean on him.

Picture that famous scene on "Only Fools and Horses" where Del-Boy leans on the bar only to find the bar flap has been lifted as he falls sideways out of view, and you can imagine what happens next.

I have absolutely no doubt the young man is standing behind me, and so relaxed as you like, hands in pockets, I slowly and gracefully lean backwards. Only when I am past the point of no return do I realise something is wrong! With reactions quicker than a speeding bullet, he dashes to my aid and catches me just before I hit the floor with my head, and gallantly lifts me straight back to my standing position. Without a word, I pick up my mug and continue my Gluwein!

Next thing, I feel a bit dizzy. Andrea is also looking slightly squiffy and being good girls we decide maybe we have had a little too much to drink to consider driving so decide to phone Mario to come and fetch us.

Andrea calls him and he agrees to come and pick us up. She comes off the phone and says he doesn't sound too pleased. I am blissfully unaware of any discord but decide I need to go to the toilet. The toilets are inside the restaurant, down a flight of stairs.

(No. you are jumping ahead!) I don't fall down the stairs. Amazing, I know! But apparently I am gone for quite a long time. All of a sudden the warmth of the indoors hits me and I feel very queasy. The sight of a toilet is too much of a temptation for my stomach and all of a sudden it says "go away" to its contents and I have no choice but to comply.

By the time I have gathered myself Mario has arrived. He is waiting for me when I emerge from the toilets, by which time I am feeling better, less whizzy-headed but very tired. He helps me up the stairs full of concern and care and steers me back outside.

Andrea is not afforded the same treatment! He is really cross with her, but again I am unaware of this fact.

Still with us is the young man who we have been drinking Gluwein with. For some strange reason they all decide that what I need is a cup of tea, and before I can resist, we are sitting in the bar waiting for tea. It arrives and although I try and suggest this is a bad idea, they all insist I should drink it.

I am, unfortunately very, very right and they are spectacularly wrong. Next thing tea hits stomach, stomach says go away immediately, tea responds and lands all across the table. I am embarrassed and they convince me no-one has noticed and start mopping it up with the paper napkins. This includes the young man who is telling me

'No, no don't worry, no-one has noticed, it's just a little tea, don't worry, everything is fine.'

Before I know it I am being whisked out and into Mario's car and whilst I start apologising and explaining that I can't understand why I feel drunk, since we were only drinking Gluwein which is very low alcohol, he will hear nothing of it and says it's all Andrea's fault for not looking after me. By now I am just tired and want to sleep. They get me back to his room and Andrea and I giggle like naughty children as she tries not to strangle me with the cross-over spaghetti straps on my nightie before putting me to bed.

Before I know it, it's morning and I feel like I've had a wonderful night's sleep and feel great. No hangover, presumably since stomach initiated evacuation procedures early enough, and I am ready for the day ahead.

I get washed and dressed and Andrea appears. She is not happy. Apparently after I went to sleep, Mario went to fetch her car and didn't return for hours. When he reappeared he was drunk and had been in the casino all evening. He blamed Andrea for not looking after me and despite her protestations that actually I am a week older than she is, he would not be persuaded!

Mario spends the day working whilst Andrea tells me all about what happened whilst I was blissfully asleep. Later, Andrea and I go to eat and I return to the container as Andrea goes to Mario's room to pack for our departure tomorrow morning.

Later in the evening we meet up in Mario's room to have a last drink together with a few other guests dropping in before we all say goodnight. Mario and Andrea seem friendly enough and we leave them and go slipping and sliding back to the container where all sleep like babes.

Next morning I am woken by my phone ringing. It's Andrea, crying, distraught and incomprehensible.

Eventually she manages to tell me she has had a row with Mario and "it's all over!" She has packed all her things into the car (including ski's so it must be serious!) and in her efforts to escape has managed to get her car stuck in the snow just along from the container.

She says she has been up for hours but didn't want to wake anyone so has spent most of the night in the car. As soon as she knew Mario had gone to work she went and collected her things and was on her way round to pick me up from the container when she got the car stuck.

I let her into the container and sit her down. She eventually calms down to a gentle sob and tells me all about the argument and how the whole love affair is over. Hmmm! Not so sure about that. It seems to be a pattern of lovers' strife followed by spectacular making up scenes any film director would be proud of. Thing is they both live out the drama in glorious Technicolor whilst the rest of us watch from the cheap seats!

However, Andrea is in no state to believe it will all have a happy ending and is desperate to ensure we are heading for the hills as soon as we can escape the perils of the snow-bound Mercedes. Trouble is, we have a problem as we discover even this car can't grip its way out of the two foot drift she has placed it in so beautifully.

Still upset by recent events, she doesn't know where to start. Mario poco, tells me there is some wood outside, so I go and find a couple of pieces and a piece of old carpet that is also lying around. He says he can't stop to help just now as he is working but will come and help us when he finishes his shift.

Placing these strategically, having first moved some snow from around the wheels, I tell Andrea to stand on one piece of wood, to stop it moving, while I try to drive it out.

I start the engine. Slowly, the car starts to move, and then slides back again. Two attempts later and Orlando appears in his car with David the French/Italian. They have just finished work.

'What is the problem?' asks Orlando.

'The car is stuck.' I reply.

'Don't worry we will soon get it out.' David says.

After a few minutes we are ready to have another go. The two boys and Andrea push, and I drive. We move a little bit but then slide back. We try again, but it slides back again. I get out of the car and tell Andrea, 'you drive, and I'll push. I am stronger than you.'

'O.k.' she says, and gets into the driving seat.

'One, two, three, PUSH!' We almost get it out.

Calling instructions to Andrea, David says again, 'one, two, three, PUSH!'

Determined this car is going to move, we all push and at the same time I try to lift the back end a little bit using the momentum to try to lift it over the snow.

"CRASH!" I hit the floor and yell out in pain.

'AARRGGHH! My knee!'

'You o.k.?' Orlando asks.

Thinking I have twisted it, I look down. I can see my left kneecap at the side of my leg. That moment of disbelief and thinking, can I get it back quickly before my brain registers the real pain passes in a few seconds until I realise 'No chance!'

'My leg, I've dislocated my knee.'

'What?' says Orlando.

'My knee, it's dislocated.'

'I don't understand.'

Great! My moment of crisis, and we suddenly develop a language problem! Remembering my recent lessons with Lucio, we have spent the last few weeks learning 'Parti della corpi.' (Parts of the body.)

'Mio ginocchio e rompere!' I say. (My knee is broken.) (We haven't done dislocate yet!)

'Broken, you joking?'

'No!'

'Oh my God! You sure?'

'Yes, it's dislocated.'

'What is dislocated?'

Still not knowing the Italian for "dislocate" I say 'rompere!' Pointing, I show the boys my knee thorough my trousers. 'Mio ginocchio e qui.' ('My knee is here!')

'You need a doctor?' Orlando asks.

'Yes and an ambulance. I have to get to hospital!'

'O.k. we go!' Jumping into David's car, they take off back to the hotel.

Andrea is standing looking at me in a state of shock and disbelief. 'Oh Gillian what has happened? Did I hit you?'

'No, the car moved and I fell, twisting my knee. It's dislocated. Don't worry I am not going to die!'

She starts to cry, and cry, and cry, and cry!!!

'Oh Gillian, I am so sorry.'

'It's o.k. Really Andrea, don't cry. Everything will be all right.'

I'll get you your coat to put around you.'

Moving to her car, she is only ten feet from me, but out of my view, I suddenly feel very alone and my leg hurts so much, for a split second I am so overwhelmed by the pain I feel sick. With no pain relief I take a deep breath and try to focus on doing something positive. Then I think. Use nature's pain relief. Slow, deep breathing to slow my heart rate down and snow! I need to get my leg cold, to stop the pain and also the swelling. Taking handfuls from around me I start to cover my knee.

Andrea puts my coat around me and continues to cry! Still helpless and in a state of shock, she takes off her own coat and puts that over me.

'Andrea, take your coat back. You will get cold.'

'No, No you take it.'

'Andrea, you are going to fall into shock. Trust me. We will both need the ambulance! Take your coat back. I am o.k. I am warm but I have to keep my leg cold.

'Why?'

'To keep the swelling down and to relieve the pain. We have to put snow on my leg, to make it cold. Help me.'

She makes a vague attempt to help me, and tries to comfort me, but ends up leaning on my leg!

'Andrea, could you move back a little bit, you are leaning on me!'

'Waaahhh.' she continues to cry!

Just at this moment, Mario poco walks up.

'What happened?' he asks.

I explain. Andrea cries!

'Why didn't you wait? I told you we would be back around two o'clock. I could have helped you!'

'Orlando and David were here. They helped us.'

'Where are they now?'

'They have gone for an ambulance.'

Moments later, they come back. 'O.k. we have called the ambulance, and the concierge will send it up to us here at the container.'

'Everyone stands around, not knowing quite what to do.

Andrea cries!

Mario poco bends down to me and gives me a hug. 'You o.k.?'

'Yes, I'm fine. Don't worry.'

'Do you want my coat around your back?'

Realising I am lying with my back against the snow, I suddenly feel a little cold. 'Yes please.' He gently helps me to lean forward, and puts his coat around me.   'What else can I do?'

'Help me put snow around my leg please.'

'Why?'

I explain.

Looking up Andrea is now sobbing uncontrollably, and shaking all over.

Next thing, Orlando appears with a quilt. Putting it around me, Mario poco gives me his thermal gloves, and then disappears. He returns with another coat for Andrea.

We chat a little bit, and I feel very safe and comfortable amongst my friends, for whom nothing is too much trouble. We share a few jokes and the time passes. After around half an hour, there is no sign of the ambulance. David and Orlando go back to the hotel to find out where it is. Just then, Mario appears in his car, still in his uniform. He gets out and is standing about twenty feet away. He looks at me, and we hold each other's gaze for a few moments. Without exchanging words, I tell him not to worry, everything is o.k. and he tells me he is mortified. Then he gets back into his car and leaves.

Andrea looks at me. 'Don't worry.' I tell her.

'But how can he leave like that?'

'He feels guilty. He'll be back, but to be honest, at the moment, I don't care.'

Orlando and David return. They have called the ambulance again. Apparently, it is stuck in traffic.

Keen to do everything possible, Orlando disappears and returns a few minutes later with a tumbler half filled with whisky. He offers it to me. 'You like?'

'I would love! But I can't. I have to have an anaesthetic.'

'Sure?'

'Sure!'

He raises the glass to me, and 'downs' the whole glass in one! Inspired by this, Mario poco disappears and returns with a tube of Pringles. (Anyone who knows me also knows I love crisps of all descriptions. Mario poco has learned this in just a few days, and I really laugh.) I tell him, 'I can't, I have to have an anaesthetic!'

'Really?'

'Yes.' He starts to eat the Pringles!

We continue to wait and I reassure everyone I am all right and not going to die!

'Anyone got a camera?' I ask.

'What!' replies Andrea.

'Anyone got a camera, we always have a camera somewhere between us, and here I am in my hour of need surrounded by all these beautiful men, attending to my every need, we should at least have a photo!'

Everyone laughs, but no one has the courage to get a camera, and although the image of the situation will remain with me as clearly as when it happened, it would have been nice to have.

Next thing, Orlando lights a cigarette. That's it! That's what I need, a cigarette! I don't smoke, but with no other pain relief, a cigarette will help. I don't want to take anything before the ambulance arrives in case it hampers anything.

'Orlando, can I have your cigarette?'

'Really, you want a cigarette?'

'Yes, please. It will help kill the pain.'

'Sure, you can.' He passes me the cigarette and I smoke it. I go a little light-headed and it takes my mind off the pain. By the time I have finished it he has started another. Half way through, I ask him,

'Orlando, can I have another?'

'Yes, of course.' He passes me his cigarette and I smoke this too! Surprisingly, I don't feel sick, or feel like I am going to pass out. The effect of the drug relieves my pain and calms me down.

161

After around another twenty minutes, a car arrives. It is Mario. Getting out he has changed out of his uniform and is crying

'I am so sorry, it is all my fault.' He says.

'Mario it is not your fault, it is just an accident and I am not going to die. They will take me to hospital and put back my knee. It is nothing serious, trust me.'

He cries uncontrollably. So does Andrea!

The perverse comedy of this situation is something like a "carry-on" film! If you made it into a film, no one would believe you. But it happened. Me, lying on the floor in agony, trying to soothe and reassure Mario and his girlfriend that everything is going to be fine, both of whom are completely useless in any practical sense and are crying as if I have died, with these other young boys doing whatever they can to help and when nothing else is possible they eat and drink! Impromptu party, 'al fresco!' It is one of the funniest situations I have ever been in!

Just then, we hear the sirens of the ambulance. Relieved that at last they are coming, we wait. Because the container is apart from the hotel and the ambulance has to be directed to us, it seems to take forever. However, eventually it arrives and a man appears by my side.

'Are you English?'

'Yes.'

'O.k. What happened?'

'We were pushing the car and I put my knee out.'

'Really! You were only pushing the car?'

'Yes.'

'Have you ever had this happen before?'

'No'

'You must be really strong to do this, just by pushing a car.'

He gives me a warm gel pack to warm my hands as my veins have sunk with the cold. Eventually he finds a vein and puts an intravenous drip in. I immediately go 'gaga' as my head swims around and everything drifts away. Next thing they straighten my leg and put me on a stretcher. I remember squealing a little bit as they moved me, but am told later it sounded like piercing wail, and everyone assumed I was in agony. I just felt completely drunk! The next thing I remember is Andrea getting into the ambulance with me and the man asking me how heavy I am. Maths is not my strong point at the best of times, but with a head feeling like I've drunk a few bottles of whisky on an empty stomach, converting stones to pounds, and then pounds to kilos is impossible. I eventually say 65 kilos. (I still have no idea if this was realistic!)

The journey seems to take forever and we seem to be travelling very slowly. (Apparently it took 45 minutes) and the next thing I feel is that I am being spun around and around. I see lots of people looking down at me and they cut my trousers off. They check me from top to toe and then tell me they are going to give me an anaesthetic and put my knee back in place.

Next thing I am away with the fairies. I feel myself falling and next thing realise I have died. I fall into a great big brain. Very colourful with lots of blood vessels. I am scared for a moment and then see Andrea and Mario floating along beside me. I look again and I see all sorts of people there too. No-one is worried and I feel reassured that being dead is not too bad. I feel myself travelling along to our destination and stop feeling afraid. There is no pain and I can see really well as we float along.

Next thing, I am being woken up. Not sure for a moment whether I am dead and arriving at the end of the journey, or am really in the world again, it takes me a while to gather myself.

As I come round I am aware of being wheeled around again, I discover later they scan and then x-ray my leg to make sure all is well, and I am then covered with blankets and a nurse comes to ask me some personal information.

163

'Can you tell me your name, address, and date of birth please?'

Bit of a struggle for me but I manage.

'Would you like to see your friends now?'

'Yes please, are they all right?'

'Yes, they are fine, but have spent the whole time crying in the waiting room, everyone thinks something terrible has happened to someone! The thing is they were so upset they couldn't remember any of your personal details!

Next thing, Andrea and Mario arrive, puffy eyes and red noses, holding hands and smiling. They start to cry again, before giving me a hug.

I then realise how cold I am, and start to shiver uncontrollably. The nurse gives me several heated blankets, but I am still cold when I reach the room I am to spend the night in. It has a spectacular view over the mountains. There is one other lady in the room, whom I later call 'Bubbles.'

A nurse asks me if I want anything, I ask for something warm to drink. She brings me some warm sweet liquid which tastes absolutely wonderful. I drink it quickly and ask for some more. After around three cups I start to warm up I am told it is 'lindenbluten' (lime flower). Andrea and Mario stay a while to chat before leaving me to rest.

The nurse brings me some food, beautifully presented, it tastes lovely and I eat the lot. I hadn't realised how hungry I am. It also helps to warm me and soon after I fall asleep. A while later Andrea returns with some bits and pieces, and my mobile phone. We are due to be back in Germany tonight and I am due to fly home from there tomorrow!

A few hasty phone calls to Jane, Jacqueline and Christine and I relax. I can't get in touch to change my flight so have to wait until tomorrow.

Mario arrives later and we all have a chat before they leave. They are friends again, and I have a beautiful view of the Alps, a comfy bed, and a very sore leg. I start to go to sleep, only to find the old lady next to me has other ideas. I spend the whole night listening to her gurgling, snoring and blowing bubbles into her oxygen mask and by the morning want to throw her head first out of the window. It's the worst night's sleep I can remember for ages.

Next morning and Andrea arrives to take me home. I now own a pair of bright turquoise crutches, and a purple foam splint which keeps my leg straight. I am also given a box of needles which I have to inject into my leg or abdomen to prevent any blood clots forming. Andrea is given instructions (in German) as to what we have to do, and we hobble to her car. It's great for me as the seats are very low, infinitely adjustable and I can stretch my leg out straight and stay very comfortable.

We return to Germany to Andrea's home and I stay there for a week learning to hobble about on crutches. I am taken to the hospital at the bottom of the hill where her home is and walk in to see a doctor who gives me a prescription for a different leg support. This one has a bendy ratchet to allow me to bend my leg a bit at a time. He is just about to take me off for an MRI scan, when I tell him I have had one in St. Moritz. It is just so like the NHS!

After a week I get a flight home and Andrea takes me to Frankfurt airport. The flight is delayed for several hours and aided by my crutches find myself adopted by a group of men who help me hobble about. The staff in the airport are horrible and don't offer me any help negotiating the intricacies involved with manoeuvring myself, my crutches and hand luggage through a scanner all in one fine movement! My new found friends rush to my aid and find me a nice comfy seat whilst ministering to my every need. Although in a departure lounge there isn't much choice for either comfort or need, but I am grateful none the less!

Christine and her partner are there to meet me at the airport and she drives my car home. We have a nice girly chat on the way back about my latest adventure.

Back home I go to the doctor and am given a note for six weeks. I ask him if I can stop the injections since my legs are really sore, and I am now covered in bruises. He says I can which is a real relief. I decide I will never be a drug addict since daily needlepoint with my flesh is really unpleasant! He calls the hospital to arrange an appointment in the osteo clinic but, "computer says no" and I have to attend A&E in person. A long wait in the hospital ensues whilst I am "processed" as a "non-urgent case" to allow me access to "continuing care." Eventually I am seen by a jolly man who tells me that if it had happened in England I would be put in plaster for two weeks, after which I would be told to walk!

Although I felt "fortunate" to have had my accident and primary care in Switzerland and then Germany, later I question whether this was actually a good idea. I suffer lots of muscle wastage to my left thigh and due to posture problems from using crutches have chronic backache, a stiff neck and sore shoulders. However I have no wish to repeat the exercise to test out the difference!

A few weeks pass and since I am not allowed to drive for six weeks and can do no exercise, I spend a long time staring at the walls. Eventually I develop a new skill of climbing them! Wholly dependent on either someone to take me out, or latterly taxis, my world becomes very small for a time, although lots of friends and my sister regularly come to my aid.

I am fortunate to find that physiotherapy is offered early to me. Although I am not seen as a priority, it appears the department has some trainees and a simple dislocated kneecap is a good and easy place to start for them.

After a couple of weeks I am given an assessment which is watched by an experienced physiotherapist. My trainee is pleased at my progress and my range of movement, especially since I am able to straighten my leg to 180 degrees.

Her mentor then comes to check and whilst asks me some questions and to make some movements with my "good leg" which includes straightening it. I happily oblige and he turns to the trainee and tells her this will prove a valuable lesson to her early on in her career about assumption. She looks puzzled. He explains to her that I have hyperextensive joints and after measuring me tells her my leg extends 15 degrees past 180, therefore my other leg will not be right until it also extends to the same degree. He also says this is probably the reason I dislocated it in the first place.

By my last visit to the physiotherapist I am driving again and feeling much more independent. As I leave the hospital car park and start to drive off I hear a nasty crunch. Getting out I find a small wall on the passenger side that I was unaware of as I parked. Driving out of the space I have turned too early and scraped the bottom of the wing by the passenger door.

Miffed, I drive to the garage I have been using for years and where I am well known. (Even the cleaner knows me now!) They tell me that the damage is quite severe since I have damaged the 'A' post along with the sill, passenger door and wing. It could be a write off! I couldn't have hit it in a worse spot, although at a glance you would never know I had had an accident.

I have a chat and decide that as I was going to change my car in the next few months anyway, I may as well do it now. Eventually, after considering all the options, I decide on a brand new car. It is the end of the month and they need to sell a couple more cars to hit the target. I get a really good deal on a new car and can pick it up in ten days.

So, with my six weeks passed I am signed off as fit for work and am ready to go back again. In twenty-something years I have never had so much sick leave and despite the long break, going back does not fill me with glee.

The first week back is hard work and very tiring, and I am relieved when the end of the week arrives.

IT NEVER RAINS...IT JUST POURS!

Saturday morning arrives and I have arranged for an Italian lesson with Lucio. I am just one hundred yards along the road from home when a car pulls out of a side street and heads straight for me.

I brake and try to steer away from it, but it is too late. "CRASH!" We both get out of our respective cars and inspect the damage. My left wing and the bonnet have been crumpled and the radiator has burst allowing the green-tinged anti-freeze liquid to spill out onto the road. A man in a nearby house has heard the noise and brings me some sweet tea and biscuits which he places on my newly-rearranged bonnet that now serves as a neat table-top! Another impromptu-al-fresco-dining-experience, this time English-style!

The man who has hit me is my post-man and apologises profusely. He asks if he can bring me his insurance documents later as he needs to finish his round. I agree and off he goes. His car seems to have less damage, although considering that he was doing around ten miles an hour and I was doing around twenty at the time of impact, I am amazed at the damage!

I can't believe it! Two accidents in a week, and my car looks like a write-off. I call the garage and the man who has sold me my new car offers to come to my aid. In my useless girly-state, I can't face getting back into my car to drive the one hundred yards back home and am frightened my car will blow up. Silly I know, but I can't help it. Fifteen minutes later and my knight in a Rover 75 arrives and drives my car back home and I follow. He arranges for someone to come and collect it on a low loader and jokes with me that the part-exchange price may be affected!

He leaves me and I call Christine and start to cry as I tell her what has happened. I also start to shake so she tells me to get a large brandy and wait at home while she drives over to comfort me.

I can't believe I have reacted in this way. I have had several bumps and scrapes over my twenty-odd years of driving (none my fault I am pleased to say!) and have never batted an eye-lid. Maybe I am getting old!

After a couple of hours of TLC from my sister I feel better and she returns home as I get ready to go out with some girlfriends for a meal. I get a taxi and once we start to eat feel much better. However, after our main course my vision starts to blur and flashing lights appear. I feel a migraine developing, but have no pain killers to hand to fend it off. Luckily one of the girls comes to my aid and after an hour I start to feel better again.

Next day I hitch a lift to church and Chris's partner, who is a solicitor, tells me to book an appointment with the doctor for next Wednesday for a stiff neck and says he will deal with my personal injury claim. Wise words, since by Wednesday my neck is so stiff and painful I don't know where to put myself.

My doctor offers to sign me off sick, but I dare not go sick again. I have only been back for a week and can't face sending in yet another sick-note! The pain however is awful and the pain killers don't seem to make any difference. Work is torture as I struggle to keep my head upright.

If Pollyanna always has something to be glad about, maybe I can count the fact that they say things come in threes to console myself. A dislocated kneecap, car damage, and a whiplash injury is my lot for the time being and I hope my run of bad luck has come to an end.

SISTERS, SISTERS

After a couple of years travelling alone, I get to a point where I take it for granted. I never feel lonely and enjoy the sense of freedom it offers me. Strange to think that the reason I first went on holiday alone was because I felt everyone was busy and that this was something that I should have to become accustomed to. How things have changed.

Following my reports of my travel several people now want to come away with me. Although tempted, any plans never seem to come to fruition. Maybe I have now become reluctant to share my little world. If anyone comes with me, the lines of distinction between home and holiday become more blurred. True, I have welcomed people to my home and introduced them to my friends, but I am still able to change things of I want to. If I take someone new on holiday with me, effectively they will be able to ride piggy-back on my pleasure train. Sounds selfish but maybe it's a safety zone I need for myself.

One exception to this is my sister. We have not been away on a proper holiday together since childhood. We have spent a few days away at friends but never a proper grown-up holiday. Christine's health has been a bit off recently. She has Multiple Sclerosis and has had a relapse and is off work sick. I invite her to come with me for a week away and she accepts. Her legs are not so good at the moment so we decide what with our luggage and the long walks getting to our destination we should hire a wheelchair. Arriving at the airport we manage to get to the check-in desk easily enough and deposit our luggage. The walk to the gate is quite far and so we set off to make sure we are not late. Walking along I instinctively step onto the moving walkway before remembering I have a wheelchair in front of me with Christine in it!

You don't realise how fast they move or how steep the lip at the end is until a time like this and as the end of the walkway approaches I tell Christine to brace herself for a bumpy landing!

Grabbing the arms of the chair we bounce onto terra firma laughing hysterically as images of Christine catapulting through the air fill our minds!

We arrive safely and spend a wonderful week together doing very little. Some days we go for a walk along the lake to the town.

We both have a good rest and fall into a regular pattern as the days pass. Each evening before getting changed for dinner we share a couple of glasses of prosecco and some nibbles on the balcony.

One evening, everyone in the hotel eats early before rushing through the gardens to the lake to watch the August firework festival. Lots of the boats are lit up and fireworks are let off across the lake. We have a lovely evening before going for a drink in the mountains.

Towards the end of the week it is Christine's birthday. I have asked for a cake to be made for her and we have dinner with Andrea and her children. At the end of our dinner the lights suddenly dim and a cake arrives. The children from the children's club appear and sing 'Happy birthday' to Christine along with the waiting staff.

It is a lovely evening and a wonderful end to a special week away. Sooner than we can blink we are packed again and on our way home. We have had a wonderful time together and both feel well and happy for the break together.

Of all my wonderful friends to have brought to my special place, I am glad it was my sister that came and I am sure our parents would be smiling down on us…

Back home and one day Christine and I decide to have a girly lunch and go and see a clairvoyant. Arriving in Birmingham we have lunch and make our way to a shop nearby. Christine has been here before. She takes after my mum who always used to go and see

'Gypsy Rose-Lee' whenever we were on holiday. Frustratingly, she never divulged what was said!

We both go in together and take notes as to what is said. I go first. The lady turns the cards and immediately tells me to leave my job!

She turns the next card and repeats, 'leave your job, it's a bad place. You need to get out. You will retrain for something which will help people and will work at a place for a time before working for yourself. You will be successful in your new career but you must leave where you are.' She then goes on to say, 'you will meet a man...' Christine and I exchange glances 'he will be someone that you know but that you don't know...'

I am confused 'What do you mean?' I ask.

'Well you will know who he is, but you don't know him very well...'

'And...?'

'...And that will be that. You will meet him somewhere like the corner of the street, you'll meet him and that will be that!'

'What do you mean?'

'That will be that, he is the one, you will meet him and that will be that!'

She goes on to tell me some more things and then speaks to Christine. As we go back down the stairs to leave she says to me again,

'Don't forget, make sure you leave your job. It's bad for you.

Strong words!

We go home and put our notes away to be retrieved another day in the future to see if anything turns out to be true...

DINO

One night, I am travelling towards Dudley to meet a couple of girlfriends at the cinema. My mobile phone bleeps. It's a message...

'How do you fancy having a 26 year old Italian lodger for a few months?'

It's from Lucio. I call him when I get to the cinema.

'What?'

'How do you fancy a 26 year old Italian lodger for a few months? He is my cousin and he wants to come over and learn English. I thought it might help your Italian.'

'Can he cook?'

'Course he can cook, he's Italian!'

'Fine then, he can come!'

'Great, I'll get back to you. I can't tell you anymore at the moment, I have had a message from my uncle, and need to find him somewhere to stay and a job. I have asked my sister's partner to see if he can get him a job as a waiter where he works as a chef in Stourbridge, so I thought you would be a good place for him to stay and help each other with your language skills.'

'Sounds great, let me know.'

A few days later and much quicker than I expect, I get a message that Dino is coming. Other information is a bit sketchy, but I have booked a few days in Riva and have only a few days to get some furniture.

Phone call to Jane. 'Can we go shopping?' (Silly question)

'Yes, no problem, when?'

'Saturday o.k.?'

'Fine where do you want to go?'

'I thought IKEA?'

'Great. See you Saturday'

So off we go. Armed with trolleys and leaving our will to live at the entrance, we wander through the maze and follow the wiggly path through the store, picking up bits and pieces as we go, before finally emerging with various tranclements and a futon!

Then we stagger to the car and after much pushing and shoving it all goes in. We squeeze ourselves in between it all and leave for home. Dropping it all off we go in search of food and spend a pleasant evening wondering what the coming months will bring.

Next day, with a bit of help, it all gets puts together, and the scene is set.

Later on in the day, I have a visit from Lucio accompanied by a young man wearing oversized shades, legs bandy enough to drive a bus through, and a gleaming white smile.

It coincides with the day that war breaks out with the allies invading Iraq. (Hope there's no link!)

'Hello, I am Dino!' he says offering his hand to shake mine.

'I am Gillian, pleased to meet you.' I reply.

He looks slightly out of kilter, and his 'Hingleesh' is not very good. Great that means my Italian will be better and anything I can say will be gratefully received! I take him and Lucio around my home pointing out various bits, and then give him a key. He is moving in, in three days and I will be away.

They leave and I pack ready to leave for a few days break.

Arriving home I walk into my home and I wonder what it will be like. It smells different, and feels different, but at least it all seems in one piece and is relatively tidy. So far, so good!

Later on Dino arrives home and we start to chat. It's a bit difficult because his English is still very poor, but at least after a few days in Italy, I have the advantage as my Italian is not bad. We mix the two and manage to have a conversation.

'Do you like pasta?' he asks.

'Ooh yes, I love pasta!'

'Would you like I cook you some?'

'Yes please, that would be lovely.'

And so began a learning experience over the cooker! To say that cooking pasta by an Italian is a long and arduous process would be a bit of an understatement. The water has to be boiled for a certain length of time, tasted on a regular basis, then, when that part of the process is over, the salt has to be added, little by little and re-tasted at regular intervals. After around twenty minutes, it's just about ready...

...to add the pasta!

Then the real close work starts. More tasting, stirring, swirling, whirling and boiling, and then, hey presto! It's ready!

We haven't even started to talk about the sauce, oh and there's the right sort of pasta, from the right part of Italy. Well I must admit Lucio was right, Dino can cook, but the kitchen is covered in condensation, the washing up bowl is overflowing, and I am now a connoisseur of the term "al-dente." It means "long-winded!"

We settle in to our new routine and after a few days, Dino comes home one day to announce that he is no longer listening to anyone else with regard to his English language, or pronunciation, since all the people he has met so far, (English and Italian) don't know how to speak English! From now on, I am his Guru!

Unfortunately there are limitations to the written word that mean I cannot share with you some of the classic word comedies we are entertained with during Dino's stay. One was his difficulty is saying 'Th' as in Thursday, but, as an English teacher in the restaurant found out one day as she remonstrated with him as he said "Tursday," Dino has the last word...

'... Th,-Th- Th' she repeats.

'T-t-t' replies Dino.'

You have to learn to say Th, in English try again' she implores.

'Excuse me madam,' says Dino handing her a bottle of beer, 'can you read this to me please?'

(This is where the written falls down as I can't write this phonetically very well.)

'Pe-row-neey nastrow azoorow' she trills with her lovely black-country twang.

'Wrong madam, it's Peroni Nastro Adzurrrro' he says rolling his 'R's' as the words dance around his tongue. 'Try again!'

'Puroni nastro azooraow' she says.

'Wrong, try again.'

'I can't do it' she declares.

'No, and I can't say Thursday, so you stick to English and I'll stick to Italian! More coffee madam?'

Although I don't want to listen to Dino's conversations on the phone, I can't help trying to listen to see if I can understand any of the words he uses. The big problem I have is "hearing" the spoken word. I really hope that during Dino's time with me I will be able to improve my ability to hear.

He tells me after one phone call home that his mother is very worried that he is under threat of being killed by one of Saddam Hussein's missiles. I reassure him that by all accounts the missiles don't travel that far, although we must remain vigilant.

Sometimes in the evenings, when he comes back and starts the pasta marathon, I wander into the kitchen and we chat. After a long day of work and English, he regularly stops and declares 'Italian break' during which we converse in Italian. Over time I really start to understand what is being spoken and get to a point where I can understand him even when I can't see his face. My defining moment comes one night when he is talking on the phone to someone in Italy and lapses into Napolitano, (allegedly one of the most difficult dialects,) and I understand perfectly what he is saying. I also get to a point where I am able to listen to conversation and understand without having to translate it in my head. On a very few very rare occasions, Dino complements me on my language skills declaring that if I was to spend three months in Italy, I would be extremely fluent. High praise indeed since macho pride prevents him from giving too many compliments!

After a couple of weeks he tells me his friend Filippo wants to come over. He is the boyfriend of Dino's girlfriend's sister! Dino secures employment for him at the restaurant, and I agree that he can stay with us for a while. Dino is not keen for Filippo to stay with us for too long, as he feels we will be overcrowded and Dino wants him to stand on his own two feet a bit.

Two weeks later and Filippo arrives. Tall, quite big build, clumsy and a complete pain in the arse!

To be fair he can be lovely, but he has been spoiled, never had to do anything for himself, his parents prefix any sentence that comes out of his mouth, and he is really lazy. He eats like a horse, and empties it out at a similar rate, having to "go for a big service" at least four times a day, a delight to which we are all informed.

Within two weeks I want to dangle him from the nearest bridge by his ankles. We develop a frustrating love-hate relationship, but mainly frustrating! We obtain a list from the local college of student accommodation locally and soon find him a room just half a mile down the road in "zee ows of Sha-ron" as it becomes known.

He settles well except for Sharon's boyfriend who Filippo finds a bit frightening for some reason. He has red hair and becomes known as 'Mr Red' Filippo seems to find his hair colour scary, and views him with scepticism. On the plus side, Sharon has a little dog and Filippo, being a great big overgrown puppy himself, finds a willing canine companion in Sharon's dog.

Although Filippo graces us with his presence on a regular basis, and occasionally stays the night, the bungalow becomes more sedate and calm without him.

If I was being kind about him I would say he is quite loving, endearingly quaint, and just like a good bottle of wine, doesn't travel well and creates nasty sediment that taints your palate when he is forced to be moved.

No matter how hard I try to educate him with social manners and common courtesy he consistently fails to learn.

One evening soon after he arrives I offer to take them to the restaurant for the start of their shift. Dino is ready and waiting, Filippo is dragging his heels. Trying to hurry him along, I point out that he will be late if he doesn't get a move on.

Shrugging his shoulders with a look of disinterested arrogance he says, 'I don't mind, this work is not important to me.'

The red mist descends and after bundling him into the car, I go mad! I lecture him on the fact that he has been welcomed into our homes, given a job to help him earn his keep and the very least he can do is show some gratitude to the people who are all looking after him. He is as dismissive as ever and says 'I don't care about these people, they are not my people, and I will soon be going back in my 'ome in Italy!'

Incensed, I tell him he will be going back in his 'ome in Italy a lot sooner if he doesn't learn some manners, and that I will not allow him to discredit me or my reputation by his disgraceful ingratitude. (Translated accordingly, although his English is actually very good so doesn't take much amendment.)

Dino takes over as I drop them off and for a while Filippo is much more polite and punctual.

Jane has much more patience with him and finds the whole scenario really funny, although even she has her sense of humour strained occasionally. Generally though the more irritating and complaining he becomes, the funnier Jane finds it all!

During the time Dino stays with me, when time allows, we go out and about around England to see the sights. If we are really unlucky, Filippo joins us! Dino is a great travelling companion, he really appreciates this part of his education and I buy him a map of England and mark with a black felt pen all our journeys. I try where possible to do circuitous routes to give him the

180

widest vision of our lovely green and pleasant land. Over a period of time, I really learn to appreciate what it is that foreign visitors see and love about our country. I get to see our country through outsiders' eyes, and it really is a very beautiful place to live and call home.

Filippo does however, give us so much pleasure when suffering his greatest discomfiture, and revenge being a dish better served cold, I get very fat on my cold dishes of revenge!

EASTER

Without doubt the best fun we have is Easter weekend. Jane, her husband, and daughter, are going to their boat at Shell Island in Wales. They invite the boys and me to go down and join them. Dino is really enthusiastic. Filippo is a groaning drudge, who becomes renamed "The Baby" by Dino by the time we return home.

Driving to Wales, the weather is beautiful. We cross the border and start to see the funny place names, which, although we all know challenge the English, completely confound the boys. Although I would never profess to be an expert, my mum was really good at English grammar and correct pronunciation was something we were brought up with. She taught my sister and myself the basics of Welsh pronunciation, and once again I find my childhood knowledge provides me with a less well used tool in my educational cupboard that I am able to dust off and crank up once more.

Filippo complains all the way there, how much further have we to go, how many more miles, are we nearly there yet...

We answer every question with an answer of either twenty minutes, or half an hour. He sleeps on and off for most of the journey and we eventually arrive across the causeway at Shell Island.

We find Jane and her family in the bar and sit down for a few drinks. The locals are really kind and make a fuss of the visitors and before we know, it is time to make our way over to the boat.

Jane's husband and a friend of his paddle back and forth a couple of times ferrying bedding, provisions etc., and before we know it we are being summoned to take our places in the tender as we are ferried across the thirty metres or so to the boat. Jodie and Jane go first, and Dino and Filippo are next.

What happens next is like something out of a comedy drama. Dino and Filippo get into the tender, and just as they are about to move off, Filippo launches himself out of the tender and back onto terra-firma! Dissolving into a complete panic, he declares he cannot possible go into this boat, and will die if forced to do so. Accompanied by appropriate arm actions, and dramatic vocals, I am instantly able to see why opera is definitely an Italian forte!

We are all a little taken aback and look at each other blankly. John takes control brilliantly. He takes off his sailing jacket and puts it on Filippo, then physically 'places' Filippo into his car, wrapping him in a blanket as he turns on the engine to warm him up, and tells him to sit still!

Dino and I are rowed over to the boat and tell Jane and Jodie what has happened. Giggling at the comedy of the situation, Jodie, who is fourteen years old, puts it all the more in context as she is standing on the boat in a T shirt incapable of understanding why Filippo is in such a state!

Still protesting he would rather 'Die than get into this little boat' John tells him if he doesn't get into it he will definitely die from hypothermia! Next thing we see is John and his friend, manhandling Filippo into the tender and they leave the shore before he can blink!

Trying not to laugh we pull him onto the boat, wrap him in a blanket and give him a stiff drink to bring him round.

One thing I do notice in all this is something I don't remember seeing before, and that is the phenomenon of phosphorescence as the oars sweep through the water creating the beautiful iridescent glow marking the trail from the boat. Especially fascinating is the effect of this as water droplets fall form the oars, and I am amazed at the amount of phosphorescence created just from a few drops of water. Nature at its beautiful best!

Safely on board we all settle down, cook some food, have a few drinks and retire to our bunks. Actually, what really happens is that we send Filippo first and we all have some fun at his expense, then we go off to bed.

Next day we go out and about around Portmadog, and amazingly Filippo, recovered from his trauma behaves impeccably, and has no trouble being transported in the tender.

After a lovely break, we leave to go home. I talk to Dino and ask him if he would like to go home by a different route, whereby he can see different countryside, and most importantly, Wales's highest peak, Snowdon. He does, but because it is a longer route home, we have to lie to 'The Baby' about it all. To be honest, any journey more than fifteen minutes creates discomfiture for him so an extra hour or so won't make too much difference!

We stop off in Portmadog for lunch at the milk bar, a café that has been there for as long as I can remember. We have steak and kidney pie and veg. The boys love it, and it's the most animated I have seen 'The Baby' for days. Hopefully it will make him sleep peacefully for a few hours.

We set off and as we do, the sun comes out, beautiful blue sky and we have the most wonderful picturesque journey back home. Stopping at the bottom of Snowdon for a photo opportunity, and 'The Baby' clearly needs his gripe water. Turning his back on the mountain, he starts taking photographs of sheep in a field. Despite us explaining the significance of this mountain, he shrugs and refuses to look, declaring, 'It's just a mountain.' We have much bigger mountains in Italy!'

'That's as maybe, but this is bloody Wales and this is as big as it gets!' Amazingly the top of the mountain is clear, courtesy of the beautiful blue cloudless sky, and as we all probably know, the chance seeing the top clear and unhindered by mist or cloud on a first time visit to Snowdon is something you would be wise to bet against.

Leaving Snowdon, we continue on our way, and whilst the baby sleeps, we plot another little detour. We do have quite a long journey home, but we are so close to Ironbridge, I feel it would be a sin to miss the opportunity to make a quick visit. Dino agrees, 'The Baby' is not informed...

...until we arrive...

...by which time, he is close to needing a feed, and grizzly. (No surprise there then!)

I stop the car and we get out to look at the bridge and take some photo's...

...Well, when I say 'we' I mean Dino and me. Filippo is steadfastly refusing to move!

'Filippo,' I say, 'this is Ironbridge, the first iron bridge in the world. This is a world heritage site, and the home of the industrial revolution. The chance of you seeing this bridge again in your life is quite small, and I have taken a lot of trouble to give you the chance to see it. Now why don't you get out of the car and take a look?'

With a face like a smacked bum, (which is very close to being literal) he replies 'it's just an old bridge. We have lots of bridges in Italy!'

Fuming gently I say, 'It might be an old bridge to you but without it you probably wouldn't be here.' (Very tempting!) 'Now get out of the car and look at the 'old bridge' before I drag you!'

Amazingly, he does. He takes a grudging photo, and then gets back in again.

Back into foetal position and forty minutes later we are home. The babe awakes and is as happy as can be! We decide after this that we will only take him out if we really have to. He clearly doesn't enjoy it, so better to leave him at home with Jane.

He does, at times want to come out to play, and one such occasion is when we go to Ludlow for the day. Jane drives, and we go over Clee Hill and stop at the top to enjoy the view. Even The Baby is in good spirits and we spend a pleasant few hours wandering around the castle and grounds, seeing The Feathers hotel, and another snapshot of England at its best.

Dino and I visit lots of places together including Stonehenge and Bath. 'The Baby' comes to Bath and is as unimpressed as usual, declaring, 'this is nothing special. We have lots of Roman baths in Italy!'

'Well, there's a surprise then! But we are in bloody England! And we've got lots of Georgian architecture to boot! You haven't got much of that in Italy have you?' Wasted breath, but I can't help myself.

LONDON

A couple of weeks before they go home we plan a trip to London. All three of us! We'll be lucky not to end up in the bloody tower.

I spend some time on-line and find some very cheap and cheerful accommodation in central London. We go down on the train, (The Baby sleeps most of the way there,) and arrive at Marylebone station. With only the bare minimum packed into a rucksack each, we hit the ground running and head off to see as much as possible.

We walk everywhere and after a wander through Hyde Park we end up at Buckingham Palace. (HA! Even Filippo can't say they have got one of those in Italy!) They are both suitably impressed and we then wander down to Westminster, and Big Ben. The interesting thing for me again is some of the other things that they find fascinating, things we Brits take for granted. Red telephone boxes, of all things, as well as the less surprising Red London bus, which I have to promise to take them on!

The weather for once is not brilliant. It is quite chilly, a bit grey and later in the afternoon starts to rain quite considerably. Unperturbed we go down to the London Eye to take a flight on the wheel. Filippo pulls one of his masterstrokes!

Bear in mind that the day Dino arrived in England, was the day we invaded Iraq. For the first few weeks, he and his family were convinced Saddam Hussein was going to personally deliver one of his missiles to our door and plant it fairly and squarely up his bottom! Although this fear subsided, the country remains on high alert and only two weeks ago, having been asked if there is anything to declare in his luggage, a man checking into a flight with Ryanair is arrested and thrown into jail for attempting an ill-timed joke about having a gun in his suitcase. It is plastered all over the news and we all go about our business with increased sobriety.

It would seem Filippo was asleep during this time!

As we wander up the ramp, we are asked if we have any sharp items in our rucksacks. No we say. Except, Filippo adds with a stupid grin, nothing sharp, just a gun at the bottom!

Red mist descends again and I go wild. I am amazed at his stupidity, and disappointed that he wasn't carted off into the wild blue yonder of a police car. The staff, I have to say, were much more tolerant and calm. They explain the need for vigilance and that his attempt at humour is a little ill-judged and having searched his rucksack, let him onto the wheel.

He can't see that he has done anything wrong. Even when I explain it to him and tell him about the man at Stansted it all goes over his head. Dino tries to calm it down and point out the error but the whole thing is lost on him. We spend most of the trip growling and scowling at one another, whilst I point out some of the sights.

When we alight, we have to decide what to do next. The weather by now is grim. The Baby is grumpy, so we end up in the marina next to the London Eye.

All very nice, but it doesn't give you much of an insight into London life! The one thing about London is that there is so much to do indoors if the weather is poor, that you can't see anywhere else, but 'The Baby' wants to look at the fish, so that's what we do!

Eventually, we emerge and the weather has started to improve. We meander up to Piccadilly Circus, and wander into a few shops. By now we are starting to get hungry, and London night-life is starting to emerge. Heading off towards Soho, we look for an eatery.

This gave me another insight of being a tourist. As Italians, they don't want to eat Italian! They want traditional English fayre. But after a good hour or so wandering the streets, the traditional English fayre is nowhere to be found! Lots of food from all over the world, especially Italy, but no decent English! How stupid is that! Although there are lots of English eateries away from where we are, there is nothing around here. Eventually we are so dizzy, Dino stops outside a Macdonald's, and says, 'shall we have a big Mac?'

'Over my dead body! No chance!' We make a decision and end up in an American bar. Home-made burgers with all the trimmings, it is actually quite good.

It is now late evening and we make our way to go to find the hotel. I have the directions and although it is only a couple of stops on the tube, we find a red London bus and jump on. They love it! Upstairs, at the front they are really happy. We ring the bell when it is time to get off and find the hotel without too much trouble.

To keep costs down, we all share a room, and in no time are asleep.

Next morning I wake up to find the room empty. I get up and have just finished getting ready when the boys appear. They have just returned from breakfast. I am livid. I can't believe it! They have been for breakfast and left me! Because I have slept late, I am too late to eat. They don't seem to think this is a problem.

Today we are heading home, but first they want to go to Portobello Road. They have seen the film Notting Hill and now want to meet the cast. Although I tell them there is nothing much to see, they won't be dissuaded, so we take another London bus and go for a wander down to Portobello. We walk all the way down to the bridge, and they seem surprised not to bump into Hugh Grant and Co! I am still cross at them for missing breakfast. Today they seem to be ganging up on me, and with a new found confidence in London life, seem to feel that I am superfluous.

Right, if that's what they want, I can do that! I follow at least ten yards behind all the way down Portobello Road, and eventually we get to the bridge where they run out of steam.

They turn and look to me for what happens next. I shrug, and ask what we are doing now. They look a bit confused, but then say they want to go back into central London. I ask if we are going on the train or back on the bus, they choose the train.

Great! They haven't experienced the underground, and I'm sure they won't have a clue.

We get into the station, and confusion starts to descend. I leave them floundering and after a while they ask me for help. I make it as difficult as possible for them but eventually I take over and buy three tickets for the right zone and we then look to get the tube.

Confused again as there are a few choices to make, I lead them to the right place. Saying very little, we get onto the tube and head off. I don't speak, and am still fuming at their attitude. I would like to say I can rise above this pettiness, but I can't. With patience as my weapon, I bide my time. After a while they ask me where to get off.

'I don't know. Where do you want to get off?'

'Where do you say?'

'No idea. Where are we going?' I start to sense disquiet in them.

'Well, I don't know' replies Dino looking a bit confused.

'Me neither. I don't know what you have planned for the day'

'I thought you had plans for us?'

'I thought I had breakfast, but I got that wrong! So, since it seems you have your plans already made, I will just follow along.'

'Gilly, please…'

'Please nothing, tell me what you want to do and I will follow on.'

'But we need to know where to get off the train!'

'Where do you want to get off?'

'I don't know, can you tell us?'

My point made and I know we are down near Westminster so I think this is a good place to get off.

The tube stops and I get off. They follow. As we come out into the daylight their confidence returns and Dino speaks to me, a serious look to his face.

'Gilly, we have a saying in Italy when people are like you. Go and boil in your own water.'

I burst out laughing, 'Dino, we have a saying in English for people like you, go and stew in your own juice. If you want to insult me, at least get the translation right!'

'I am sorry,' he says.

'I forgive you, but I have to tell you, I have put a lot of effort into making your time here in England a valuable experience. I have welcomed you into my home, introduced you to my family and friends and given you a real taste of English life. I am well aware that I have learned things from you too, but I think the least you can do is to show me some respect. The way you two have behaved today has been appalling.'

He apologises and gives me a hug.

We make our way back to Marylebone, taking in a few more sights along the way and get the train home. Filippo barely squeaks, grunts or groans all the way back, and true to form, sleeps for most of the journey.

Arriving back into Stourbridge, Jane is waiting to pick us up, big smile and a joyous wave. Seconds later we are in her car and she says brightly, 'had a good time?'

Long silence!

Jane starts to laugh! 'Bit too close for comfort?'

'You could say that! Tell you later.'

'Fancy a cuppa and a piece of cake?'

'Sounds lovely!'

Not that we need to go far from home for them to get the steam blasting from between my ears again.

A LESSON IN ENGLISH MANNERS…
AND A BIKE!

On another occasion, Jane invites us all to her house one evening for a meal with her and her family. Another chance to see English people 'au natural.' Only problem is there is no sign of the guests! Well, well, there's a surprise!

One of the things we really do learn about our European visitors, is that time is of little consequence. They arrive "sometime," but not necessarily "at the right time!" However, I have given them strict instructions to be home at seven fifteen prompt, in order that we can get to Jane's for seven thirty. (I don't, of course, tell them she expects us a seven forty five) Seven fifteen arrives and goes, no worry, I wait until seven thirty, still no sign. By seven forty five the steam is starting to flow, and by five to eight I am ready to kill! I call Jane who starts laughing, and tells me not to worry, she'll just delay things for a while. Meantime I go out in search.

I know they have gone to play 5-a-side football in nearby Kinver, as they do most Thursday's. Not a problem, but they were asked well in advance if they wanted to go and have a meal with Jane, and were more than happy to do so. I offered to pick them up so that they were not relying on transport, but they said, 'no problem' they would be back in more than good time. Wrong!

Leaving a note in the hall telling them in no uncertain terms that we are late and they are in the dog-house, I go to see if I can find them at the house of the person they have travelled with. No-one there!

I get back home at ten past eight and they have just arrived. My face like thunder I don't need to say anything. Like naughty children, they try hard to be nice to me, but I am having none of it. They get ready immediately and we get into the car.

Doing around 30 mph in first gear, they draw breath! 'Gilly, is everything o.k.?'

'O.k.? No, not really, you are both incredibly rude not being ready on time. Jane has gone to an awful lot of trouble to prepare a meal in your honour, and you can't be bothered enough to turn up on time.'

'We are very sorry.' Says Dino.

'It's no good telling me that, you two owe Jane and her family a big apology.'

Arriving at Jane's they seem suitably abashed. Jane comes to the door and they apologise profusely for their inconsiderate behaviour. Jane plays along by appearing suitably disappointed with them and invites them in.

Crash!

We all stop and look round, Filippo has somehow managed to walk straight over the milk bottles left out for the milk-man, and they shatter all over the doorstep!

For a few moments, he looks petrified. Justice metered out, we laugh in exasperation and after clearing up the mess, go inside and share a happy meal.

The restaurant they work in is around three miles from home. Dino has been lent a bike by his cousin for travelling about on. Filippo has no such luxury. Whilst we are at Jane's one day, Jane offers to lend Filippo a bike. It belongs to her son and is a really expensive bike. We get him a lock and chain and he is mobile!

One evening, Dino is missing. Although I am not his keeper, I get to know his routine and habits, and his absence is odd. Eventually the phone rings. It's Dino.

'Gilly, we have a bit of a problem.'

'What's the matter?'

'I am at the 'ows' of Sharon with Pippo' (one of Filippo's nickname's along with 'Pipponissimo' which was a name I gave him once when he was being a pain. The term 'issimo' attached to Italian words means 'most.' So it means the 'most Pippo' there is. Basically big pain in the bum!)

'What's wrong?'

'Nothing terrible, but can you come down please?'

'Yes, no problem, I'll be there in five minutes.'

Arriving at the 'ows of Sharon' Dino opens the front door. Whispering, and with a wry grin, he says, 'promise not to laugh when Pippo tells you, he's really upset!'

'When he tells me what?' I whisper back.

'Wait and see, just don't laugh!'

'O.k.'

Leading me up to Pippo's room, Pippo is lying on his bed looking thoroughly miserable. The weight of the world on his shoulders.

Feeling unusually compassionate towards him, I ask 'Pippo, what on earth is wrong, surely it can't be that bad?'

(I'll try this phonetically, as it is so much more effective)

'Gill-le , I av one big prob-lem.'

'What is it?'

'I av looz-ed Jane-ez bike'

'How?'

'O it iz very terrible, I av leave it in the door at the restaurant, and when I go back, iz gone.'

'Filippo, you did lock it up didn't you?'

Looking shamefaced he says 'no, I av leave it without lock.'

'You idiot!'

'I know, iss just that I tink iss safe ere. These people oo live in Stourbridge are very nice people and I don't tink they taker my bike.'

'Well you got that wrong, didn't you!'

Dino helps him out. 'Gilly we spent all afternoon looking everywhere for the bike, my feet hurt like boom boom, but we don't find it. So we go to the police station to tell them about it.'

'Right, what did they say?'

'They laugh at me!' cries Filippo.

'Laugh? Why?'

Dino smirks.

Filippo says, 'Well I am so upset I forget my English and so I can't make them understand. All I can say to them is 'before I ad a bike... and now I 'avn't! And they laugh at me, I think these people are very rude!

'I burst out laughing. Filippo is really cross.

'Now you laugh at me. Why do you laugh when it is seri-oos?'

'Pippo, it sounds so funny!'

'But what about the bike?

'Well, you lost it, so you are going to have to sort it out. You will have to go and see Jane and tell her what happened.'

'But she will be very angry.'

'You should have thought of that before you left the bike unlocked, and you need to work out how you are going to replace it.'

'I will ask my parents, they will send me money.'

'But that's not the point, you have lost something that has been loaned to you in good faith, and part of your responsibility is to look after it and return it. You can't go through life thinking that your parents or money will sort everything out for you. You have to take responsibility for yourself and your own actions, so let's go and see Jane.

We all pile into the car and head off round to Jane's. She is as usual pleased to see us, invites us in and puts the kettle on for a cup of tea. Filippo, as you can imagine, was always different, standing firm in his Italian roots, he brought to England with him, an electric espresso maker, (complete with the wrong type of plug and no adaptor,) his favourite coffee and most of the time makes his own coffee. On this occasion he politely accepts Jane's tea!

After tea is poured, Jane starts to realise all is not well. Filippo admits he has something to tell her. He blurts out all of a rush, 'Jane I 'av looz-ed John's bike. I am very sorry and I will get the money to get another one. I am very sorry.'

Jane asks what happened and the whole sorry tale is replayed again. Eventually Jane asks if he had it locked, and shamefaced he admits he hadn't. He then tells her what happened at the police station.

'Jane, I av forget all my English. I 'av tell the police, before I 'av a bike... and now I avn't!'

The pain of it all is still etched into his face.

'Say that again' she says, and as he finishes, she bursts out laughing! She sets me off and then Dino joins in. The only person not laughing is Pippo. We end up crying with laughter and at the idea of how much fun the police must have had with it all!

Eventually, Jane clams down and tells him about how important it is to look after things and that he should never leave a bike unlocked. Filippo asks how much she wants to replace the bike. She says since it is not her bike, he will need to ask her son. Right on cue, he arrives home. Jane tells Filippo to tell him what has happened and at the end, we all end up in stitches again. Jane's son says that he hasn't used his bike for a long time and agrees to accept a small payment by means of compensation. We then agree to stop making Pippo squirm.

More tea and a piece of cake and we head off home.

The boys go to work, and I make myself something to eat. The phone rings and it's the police. A very nice police woman asks me if I know Filippo and have I heard about the bike.

'Oh yes, I have. I've also heard what he told you when he lost his language ability.'

She starts to laugh and tells me it's the most fun they have had in a while. She explains that the chances of finding the bike are slim, and I tell her not to worry, Filippo had learnt a valuable lesson, (we hope) and we have all had a good laugh at his expense!

TIME TO GO HOME AND A TRIP UP NORTH

Before we all know it the time for them to go home fast approaches and Dino and I plan a trip around the north of England. I work out a plan to go up through the Lake District, into Scotland, across and up to John-O-Groats, down to Edinburgh, and back home again. All in five days!

Dino takes the last week off work and I take him on a whistle-stop tour of the Lakes and Scotland. Jane agrees to baby sit Filippo and she is going to arrange a party for the night we come home.

The week before we go to Scotland, Jane invites us round for a few drinks. She has a gift for Dino of an integrated tea-cup and tea-pot from Portmerian pottery as a memento of English life and his stay with us. He loves it! All the time he has been in England, Dino has tried to live the English life and always drinks tea as opposed to coffee. As we reminisce about the time they have spent here, Dino says

'Gill, Jane, I have a question to ask you.'

'Yes?'

'Well, since I have been in England, there is one thing I have not seen, and it is something you are supposed to be famous for.'

'What's that then?'

'It's the English humour. They say that the English have a wonderful sense of humour, but since I have been here, I have not seen it like I thought I would.'

'But Dino, we have been taking the piss out of you since the day you arrived!' Jane replies.

We fall about laughing, Dino looks confused!

'I tell you what, from now on, every time we are taking the p***, we'll tell you, "English humour", how's that?' I say.

'Yes, thank you!'

And we do…constantly…and he still only gets it occasionally…!

A few days later and we set off early and head towards the Lakes. Another beautiful day emerges which fortunately turns into another beautiful week. The weather, to which any visitor would vouch, can make or break a lifelong impression. We travel through all the usual places, along Lake Windermere, before crossing over to Hawkshead where we stop for lunch. Again Dino wants to try the local food and I have some wonderful trout, and he has lamb.

Refreshed, we travel on and eventually arrive at the bottom of the Hardnott Pass. If you've ever driven over it, you'll understand it's not for the faint-hearted. I have an inherent fear of falling off the edge of things, and the Hardnott Pass is not somewhere you want to fall off the side of. However, the reward for travelling up this windy, narrow road on a clear day is spectacular, and one of the most beautiful views you can experience. If it was one-way it wouldn't be so bad, you could just put your foot down and keep going, but of course, it isn't, and although there are passing places, it awakens another of my other fears which is falling backwards.

Doing a hill start on a one in three gradient, tests all my faith in modern car engineering, physics and my self-belief that I can do a hill start without rolling backwards into the abyss!

Then there are the sheep that see me coming and stroll across the road just to pull faces at me and laugh at my discomfiture. Although this may be a bit dramatic, I remember many years ago, going over the pass in a one litre Vauxhall nova, and having to stop several times on the way to let the engine cool down, so I do have past experience to fuel my anxiety. Added to which, as children, my dad would relish driving our Morris Oxford up roads marked 'steep gradient, unsuitable for motor vehicles.' Sometimes the roads were so steep and I was so small that I could only see the windscreen wipers and bonnet from the back seat. Holding my breath and keeping rigidly still seemed the only way to will us to safety.

So, here we are. Dino is aware of my trepidation, but facing my fear and doing it anyway, (as the famous self-help book tells us) off we go! The first part is not too bad, and I even manage to stop twice, willingly, to take some photos. Then the road gets steeper and my knuckles get whiter. We are doing well until a car comes down to pass us. I pull over. As we have stopped we take another chance to look at the scenery. As we make to move off Dino offers to take the wheel.

'Why don't you let me drive, I am used to these sort of roads, we have lots of them in Italy.'

I am very unsure, but he persists.

Taking the balanced view that he is a qualified driver, and as this is a single track road so there is very little danger of him driving on the wrong side, and there is very little traffic about, and that he has driven a little in England before, I concede. Just until we get to the top.

Wrong decision!

We are doing well, but then just as we get to the top, a car is coming the other way. Dino moves to the left to allow the car to pass, and there is a nasty popping sound, followed by a hiss.

We move off to the top of the pass where there is more room to park. We get out and the front tyre is going down rapidly!

Bugger! Oh well, we just have to change it. One skill I do possess is the ability to change a car tyre. Dino also possesses the same skill so we have nothing to worry about...Except that the first thing you need to do is loosen the nuts, which also involves removing the locking wheel nut. Can't do it! Can't find the contraption to get it off and have no useful tool that will help. Try the mobile phone to call the AA. No signal. Emergency only, says my phone display. Oh well, this feels quite high on my emergency agenda. Time is getting on and it's a bloody long walk down the road to civilisation. Try emergency. Nothing, no signal. Great back up that is then! Looks like the long walk is beckoning.

The sheep are having a great time, rolling round the heather laughing, holding their sides to stop them splitting, I am sure one of them looks familiar. I bet it's a relative of Filippo, which would account for his fascination with sheep and all the photos he has taken. They are probably cousins, and now he has exacted his revenge on me for laughing about his bike!

Realising I am now starting to hallucinate, (must be all this fresh mountain air,) I have been distracted, and hey presto, Dino has come up trumps. He has managed to get the nut off and quick as you like we have changed the tyre. It's one of those narrow tyres that gets you back on the road, so will need to be replaced as soon as possible.

Curiously, this has temporarily cured me of my fears, and we are both happy for me to take the helm again. Reaching civilisation again, is a blessed relief, and we wend our way to Keswick and our resting place for the night.

Next day, we find a garage to get the tyre changed. The man in the garage tells me that the tyres on my car are obsolete, but fortunately he has one that is compatible, and before you know it we are back on the road.

I am not sure whether it is because I am still a little traumatised from yesterday, but the car doesn't feel quite right. It feels quite heavy and I feel as though it is pulling to the right.

A couple of weeks later, back home, I go to me local tyre garage and he tells me what I feared. The new tyre is incompatible with my other tyres, and will need to be changed! Even more strangely, he is amazed that I have been told my tyres are obsolete, and orders one in to be delivered within twenty four hours. My car feels so much better afterwards although my purse is a little lighter!

Back to the Lakes, and day two of the trip. We travel on and cross the border into Scotland. Along the side of Loch Lomand, we stop at a little village for a photo opportunity and come across a Scottish piper. In national costume he is there to entertain the tourists and raise a few pounds for charity. There are a few tourist gift shops and Dino has a wander around. Sometime later as we are on the road he asks me if there is anywhere that we are able to buy a set of antlers.

Quick scan of the grey matter and, unsurprisingly, I haven't got a clue! Maybe Scottish yellow pages have a listing, antler supplies? Maybe not! I tell him we can keep our eyes open and see what we can find.

Eventually we travel over Glen Coe and down into the valley along Kinlochleven. This later became well known as the place where Harry Potter goes flying. Driving on we arrive at Fort William and the Glenfinnan railway viaduct. I have made a sort of itinerary, and this bridge is on my list. Unfortunately Harry Potter got there first as they are filming the second film and we have to wait until the end of the day's filming before we can get close by. We have a wander about, go and see the bridge and head off to find our B&B for the night.

I have chosen to pre-book some accommodation to save wasting time looking for places to stay. This one looked really nice on the internet, old oak panelling, big open fires and some good Scottish hospitality.

Well, it certainly has all those things but unfortunately it is all a bit out of date. 'In need of a little sympathetic renovation, retaining many original character features and offering a unique potential for the discerning purchaser,' would be the way any estate agent would market it! Dino sums it up much more succinctly as we go into the village to eat. We get some distinctly strange looks as we walk in.

'Gillian, this place is what has been left after the nuclear bomb has gone off!'

In fact, we have a really lovely meal in the local restaurant. Locally produced venison served with fresh vegetables. As long as we don't turn the lights out we won't notice the faint glow that radiates from it all!

205

To be fair, the locals probably don't get that many tourists. The village is out of the way and not somewhere you would stumble across, Add to this Dino arriving with his big shades, they are probably as perturbed by him as we are by them!

Back at the B&B it is quite late and a beautiful clear night sky. Dino suddenly starts looking at the sky a bit puzzled.

'You can really see the stars here can't you. There is no light pollution which is so rare now.' I say.

'Yes, yes, but the sky…, is not black…, is still only dark blue…., and is nearly midnight... I don't understand. I have never seen this before!' says Dino.

'Ah, of course, you live so much nearer to the equator you never get to see a midnight sky like we have here. The further north you go the lighter it gets in summer.'

He is amazed and sits for a while looking at the night sky. I can't help thinking, another wondrous thing we have in England!

Next day after another English breakfast we retrace our path along the loch and again stop for another photo opportunity. The loch is like a mill-pond and the mountain reflections are perfect. No ripples to break the mirror, it is truly beautiful.

A long day today, we are off to Loch Ness in search of the monster, and then up to John-O-Groats and back again to spend the night on the side of the loch.

Going back to my childhood again, we spent many times travelling up the east coast of Scotland, as we had a caravan at Bridlington. On one trip, we drove all the way up to the top of Scotland, and at the end of the road that leads to John-O-Groats, my dad decided there was no point going there, just for the sake of saying we'd been to John-O-Groats, so he turned round and drove back!

There can't be too many people who travel all that way and then turn around, so that may be one claim to fame, but I have always wished we had travelled those extra few miles just to say I have been. I have been to Land's End, and widely travelled around Britain, so it is only right and proper to have gone to John-O-Groats.

Crossing the bridge at Inverness, we follow the A9 to Tarlogie and the landscape changes quite dramatically and I feel it becomes really hard work. Following the road along the coast, there is mainly just scrub and the off-shore oil-rigs for company. I really feel we are going uphill. Pressing on without stopping, we eventually reach the point where we take a right turn to John-O-Groats. Remembering vividly the last time I was here around twenty five years ago, this time I take the turn and we are on our way.

Hindsight is such a wonderful thing! The first indicator is the view in front of an extremely straight and uninteresting road. After what seems an age we arrive at the top of Scotland. What a disappointment! The bleakness is fine, very levelling and given the opportunity to appreciate this bleakness I am sure it would be very therapeutic. Shame it is spoilt by some cheapy-tacky shops, and just to cap it all, a cheapy-tacky bride all meringued up in her superbly-chosen-perfect-for-the-occasion-wedding-gown. Each to their own and it wouldn't do for us all to be the same, but with such a bleak outlook as a landscape from which to start married life, it wouldn't be my idea of a good omen!

Hopefully all the dreams are coming true for the new Mr and Mrs Whoever, and it certainly gave Dino another insight into the quirky behaviour of us Brits!

Leaving John-O-Groats, we stop at Wick for a bite to eat, before heading back to Loch Ness where we stay at a B&B on the side of the loch.

Next morning at breakfast, I ask the landlady if she knows anywhere that we can get some antlers. She suggests the deerstalker at the deer farm may have some.

She directs me to the deer farm, which is just half a mile behind the B&B. Following her instructions we travel along a narrow road for a mile or so and pass through a gate over a cattle grid. Following the road along the landscape, aided by another clear blue sky and a bright and glorious dose of sunshine, it opens out to one of the most beautiful places I have ever been to in my life.

I couldn't possibly put into words the beauty of this place and do it justice. Suffice to say that we get out of the car on a narrow road in a wide valley at the bottom of two spectacular mountains and Dino asks me 'Where is the deer farm?'

'This is the farm' I reply, holding my hands out wide.

As we meander along the valley bottom listening to the babbling stream we stop frequently and look for the deer. Wandering discretely over the mountain side barely visible are herds of wild deer. They blend so naturally you can only really see them when they move. We follow the road until the end and meet a huge and very dramatic dam. Conversely blending and contrasting with the landscape, it is beautiful.

We turn around and drive slowly back eventually ending up at the bottom of a long drive that leads to the deerstalker's house. We pause before driving slowly up to the cottage. Two dogs come to greet us noisily with big waggy tails, but undoubtedly big waggy teeth hidden behind big waggy jaws!

I tell Dino to let me do the talking, and to keep his designer shades off his designer face!

I get out of the car and a man walks towards me looking nervy. As he approaches, I explain the reason why I am here. I tell him that my passenger is Italian and that the antler symbol is very lucky in Italy. I ask him if he has any antlers that I could buy from him. He looks at me suspiciously, and looks towards the car where Dino is standing outside looking completely out of place, then back to me again. He tells me that the culling season doesn't start for a few months, so antlers are not really available at the moment. I ask him if it would be possible to contact me when the season starts so that I can come back to collect a set of antlers. He studies me again and asks where I am from. I tell him, south of Birmingham. He looks surprised, and says, 'What? would you come all this way for a pair of antlers?'

'Yes, they have a very special meaning so it would be worth the trip up here.'

He pauses and then says, 'Go down to the gate and wait there for me. I may have a set in my shed left from last year, but I'm not sure. Wait there for half an hour and if I find any I'll bring them down.'

'Thank you.' I say. I turn to go and as I walk back to the car he says. 'Oh, by the way, have a look in the sky down by the gate. You may see some golden eagles!'

We wait and watch, and we see the golden eagles, very high up, and to be honest if he hadn't told us what they were I would never have recognised what they were. So high above, but unquestionably big birds of prey, they glide along the thermals looking for prey. Then we hear an engine and looking up see a Landrover approaching. He pulls up alongside us and produces a huge set of antlers.

Dino's face lights up and the deerstalker smiles. I give him twenty pounds which he attempts to refuse, but eventually accepts as I explain how grateful and appreciative we are and I hope he understands what a special gift he has allowed us.

Putting them onto the back seat of the car we head off towards our next destination. Edinburgh.

I haven't been to Edinburgh for many years, but am amazed to find that I remember my way down to Queensferry for a really good view of the two bridges. I tell Dino the story of the never-ending painting Forth Bridge, take a few photos and head off to find our hotel. Quick change and off we go along Princes Street for a bit of window shopping, then on to the fish restaurant my sister has told me about, before finishing off in a bar where Dino samples some different whiskies to get a proper flavour of Scotland!

Next morning and we take a quick trip around the castle, buy a couple of souvenirs, and we are back on the road for a not so quick trip back down to Stourbridge!

Dino enjoys the hustle and bustle of Edinburgh, so it is a good place to visit as his last memory of Scotland.

Heading back home through the beautiful Scottish landscape, and I start to feel very tired. We stop at a petrol station and I make a big mistake and have some Cadbury's chocolate shots. After five minutes I feel more awake and feel great until half an hour later when my sugar levels drop and I feel ill! Lots of water to give me a kick and within another half hour I am feeling better. Stopping again only for a comfort break we eventually arrive home around six o'clock.

A FOND FAREWELL

With no time to catch a breath, Jane has arranged and organised a feast of food and wine for a farewell party. Dino's family from England arrive along with acquaintances he has made since he arrived. A few of the people who work at the restaurant appear after the restaurant closes, including Simone and his partner Sonia, and a little Portuguese guy whose name escapes me, but made a wonderful impression after spilling red wine all over his white shirt and looked like someone has stabbed him in a Die Hard film.

Simone and Sonia have also become endearing, they have been in England for several years, taken private English lessons, and in spite of these things have been hardly anywhere and still struggle with the language! Sonia is particularly funny as her accent has developed into Chinese-sounding English which Jane mimics perfectly.

Eventually, my tiredness overwhelms me and I go to find a quiet corner to go to sleep. Tomorrow Jane and I are taking the boys to Gatwick for their journey home.

Next morning, and I am feeling very refreshed, Jane definitely isn't! She stayed up very late and having had an unusual amount of alcohol looks and feels terrible. As a true friend, she is determined to accompany me to the airport, and after propping her up in the car with a pillow to rest her head on, we set off. A bit cramped, but with everything on board we arrive safely and go to check in. The antlers by now seem to have grown as they have been wrapped and bound in bubble-wrap, brown paper and lots of string and sellotape. The airport staff point us to the belt for strange and unusual objects and promise to take care of them.

We all go to find somewhere to eat and while the three of us have a final traditional English breakfast together, (something they have become quite fond of,) Jane wanders off for twenty minutes since her stomach

211

and brain have not yet become settled enough to tolerate the thought and smell of freshly cooked bacon and eggs.

Eventually we wave goodbye and Jane and I set off on our journey home. By now we are both exhausted. The sun is shining and as soon as we are able, we pull off the M25 and find a pub car park. Pulling up we recline our seats and have forty winks.

Two hours later and we wake up again and are ready to go home. We listen to the Simply Red song 'Home' and reflect on the pleasure we have had for the last three months.

Although they were only with us for three months, we have had a great time. The sun came out on the first morning Dino arrived, and it never went in until after he went home. It was wonderful to be able to show off our lovely country at its bright and shiny best. One afternoon we were at the top of Jane's huge garden watching the squirrels and listening to the birds and she said to me, 'Hasn't this been a wonderful spring. I'm sure it will be one we will look back on and remember as something we can't quite believe happened.'

Now it's back to the real world again and we return to normality. I am grateful to have my home back to myself again. I have enjoyed the experience but have started to miss the peace and quiet that my life affords me.

There is something else that I have learned from all this which is that the more I travel, the more English I become. Having seen England from a view of foreign eyes, I see more and more what it is that makes our country so beautiful and attractive to foreign visitors. I have spent quite a lot of time travelling abroad recently but still love home better than anywhere else. We have so much enjoyment, usually at the boys' expense, and in many ways life is very carefree.

There is just one blot on the landscape…and it is rather a large one…

WORK (With a capital W!)

Wouldn't it be great if you could write something down in all innocence, make a bet on it happening, and then collect the winnings at a million or so to one!

On the other hand, how is it that some things come back not just to haunt you, but to bite you on the bum so hard the teeth marks stay visible for years to come and the scars heal very slowly!

Guess which one I did?

Yep! Sore bum!

So hereby hangs a tale. It's my great escape from the umbilical cord I talked about earlier called The Civil Service.

Writing this episode is quite difficult. Not because of the experience, although it was a particularly harrowing time for me, but because I am still not sure exactly what it was all about. I therefore tell this tale with the emphasis being very much 'my side of the story.'

There have been a few times in my civil service life that have been particularly enjoyable. If I was being cynical I could just say less miserable.

No, to be fair I have had some really fun times in Her Majesty's service. Unfortunately this was not one of them.

Our office has always been a bit of a mismatch with others in our group and we are often left to manage the general day-to-day running of things by a distant and disinterested higher management. Definitely a black sheep as far as our district manager is concerned, he rarely disguises his palpable contempt for those bar*****s at Kidderminster.

I'm not sure how it all started, but suffice to say, I never saw it coming. I have my suspicions but can't say for sure. But imagine if you will, I am working happily as an indoor visiting officer (only in the civil service!) and have the best group of staff to work with that I ever

213

had the pleasure to supervise in my career. We work really well as a team, support one another and are wholly loyal to each other. Everyone works to their strengths and there are no power struggles. Although I am supervisor, I always describe myself as being paid a different salary to perform a different job description. I cannot work without the team, but they can work well without me. I have always believed in trying to empower and teach people to perform their role so well that they can do the job better than I can. It may mean I make my role redundant, but that is all to the good. In the 'old days' in the service, supervisors were seen as fountains of knowledge for the teams they led. If you didn't know the answer, the supervisor did.

Times changed along with supervisor roles. The job descriptions altered and supervisors became responsible for managing the targets so set by the government, implementing changes no-one liked or approved of, managing staffing, budgets and of course, service delivery. The public came somewhere at the bottom of the list along with paying out some good-old tax-payers lolly!

So, our team are responsible for making savings as a consequence of our 'intervention.' We can 'intervene' in several ways, including visiting (our primary role) or by telephone interventions. We are given targets for various types of claims, and have to ensure we are making savings for the government to announce proudly in parliament as and when they need to make an impression on the public they believe hang on their every word, (which of course they do!)

The problem is, (and you may find this difficult to accept as a problem) we are really good at it, in fact we are not just good, we are quite brilliant, and this starts to be a problem. Adding to our problem is that our manager, who has a lead role across our district of around four offices for 'interventions,' becomes a proverbial 'fly in the ointment.' To be honest she becomes a real 'pain in the a**e!'

214

The fundamental problem seems to be that she wants to make improvements so that she can go and scoop up some brownie points at management meetings and put some feathers in her promotional headgear. Trouble is, she has no practical knowledge or application of what we do, and instead of using us to work with her, she manages to spectacularly upset the apple cart and alienate herself from us. It is a wonderful example of a loose cannon with a little knowledge being a dangerous thing. We have spent a good deal of time working out the most effective and profitable ways of making savings and we are as slick as Torvill and Dean performing Bolero! O.k. maybe not quite that good but we are very efficient. That's not to say that we have become ostrich-like and think we know it all, and we are always looking for ways to improve but our boss is still in the learner seat while we are front row in the Grand Prix! ...And... we have a secret and wonderful weapon... Donna!

Donna is brilliant, leaves nothing to chance and never takes a short cut. She is cunning, calculated and has every one of her lovely fingers on the intervention statistics pulse! She is in constant touch with all the other offices to find out what they are up to and using her local knowledge of our area and clientele, knows exactly what works and what doesn't. She has tried all the ideas everyone else has used, and invented lots more of her own. Added to this is her absolute integrity. She is very capable of interpreting the guidelines and instructions to the stretchiest point, but she will never cheat. Donna keeps her eye on the boys who are out visiting, and decides who they need to see, when, where and the most cost-effective way of doing it all. She has the targets and taking into account annual leave, seasonal changes and adjustments, makes a yearly plan which is then divided into a weekly or monthly activity. I add to this by doing office interventions and between us we achieve exactly what is asked of us, with a little extra for good measure.

Sandra, our boss should be really happy, but she isn't. She wants to come up with something we haven't

215

thought of or tried before. To be fair, we would be more than happy for her to find something, but every time she has an idea, we have a tried and tested reason why it's a bad idea. We consider going along with some of her ideas, but since we are so tight on time and resources, we can't afford to.

Sometimes, she goes off to another office and bounces in with what they do at such-and-such an office. We respond with, tried it, doesn't work, can't because their client base is different to ours, or can't do that it's against the rules, none of which brings a cheery smile to her face.

Why oh why she can't just be happy that we are delivering the savings and improved accuracy as demanded, and take credit for having a good team I really can't say, but she seems intent on trying to cause trouble.

Her next tactic is divide and rule. Big mistake! Unfortunately for her, we are such a good team we all support and defend one another. She tries to get me to 'encourage' the team by various means and ideas, and when that fails, she tries to get the team working against me. Another bad idea, she just succeeds in making us even more cohesive.

Eventually she seems to give up and just treats us with thinly veiled contempt.

One day it all gets too much for her and she explodes, but as usual falls spectacularly on her face.

One of the best things about my time in the civil service is flexi-time. The thing about working for the government is that they have to make sure all their wonderful policies apply to their staff, and we have always seemed to lead the way. We were at the forefront with family-friendly policies, sick leave, flexible working, career breaks, part-time working and job-sharing to name but a few. But my favourite is flexi working hours. It has worked really well for me. I work up my hours and then take time off in lieu. Nothing difficult there. But Sandra becomes annoyed that I use it to its full potential as allowed, which means I take around two days off a month, and often go away for a break.

One week there is some national controversy that the union are engaged with and a two day strike is called. I decide to go on strike, and having already arranged for two days flex time off, as well as not working Friday's and a weekend in between, it means I get a week off without using any annual leave. I book a flight and a room and am heading off to Italy.

Although there is absolutely nothing wrong with what I am doing, Sandra finds out and throws a big grizzly bear out of her cot. She phones me and accuses me of abandoning the section saying, and I quote, 'in any case I think you have too much leave!'

I am savage! 'I am entitled to take my allocation of annual leave which you can check is no more and no less than I am allowed. I have already had my flexi leave agreed and I have no need to tell you if I am to go on strike. Indeed the union would respond very strongly of any threat or intimidation.'

'Well, I want to see you and Tim after the meeting this afternoon.'

The problem for her is that Tim is on annual leave during the strike, but with most of my team on strike too and with me now going on strike there is no supervisor cover on our section. No big deal really, but it just makes Sandra really cross for some reason.

We have our meeting and afterwards Tim and I stay behind. Sandra lets fly and accuses us of mismanaging the section and then starts verbally assaulting me. Thankfully Tim is there and after a few minutes takes control. He stands up and says to Sandra, 'You, shut-up.' Turning to me he said 'You go!' We both do as we are told!

Into the scenario arrives Ann. She is another supervisor and is a character all of her own. They definitely broke the mould with Ann. Together with

217

another couple of girls we have worked together as supervisors for many years.

I go to find Ann and take her off upstairs. The building is seven stories tall, and having spent years looking after the maintenance of it, I know it like the back of my hand. I tell Ann what has happened and we are both absolutely shocked. I have never been spoken to in such an inappropriate or unprofessional manner in all my working life, and coming from my manager is so out of order I don't quite know what to do. Shaking, I tell Ann I am o.k. and send her back before she is missed. I keep out of the way.

I know Sandra has to leave the office at three thirty and as tomorrow is the weekend. (I work some Fridays as it is a convenient day for meetings and if I have nothing planned it helps me build up my flexi-time sometimes.) I decide to keep out of the way until I know she has left the office. I hope she will worry all weekend and think about what she has done.

Keeping close to the stair-well a few floors up, I wait. I hear Sandra come onto the stairs and hear her telling someone about what has happened. Big mistake! The person she is telling firstly is the same grade as me but with a big brown-nose, and secondly, Sandra is discussing a personal issue with someone who is completely irrelevant. Any possible ounce of respect that I may have dredged up for her evaporates at that moment and any doubts I have about myself are dissolved. The only thing I am pleased about is hearing Sandra say, 'I can't find her, and I've got to go now, so I won't be able to see her 'till Monday. I'm really upset and it's going to spoil my weekend.'

'Good!' I think!

After a little while I go back down to my desk. We have a chat amongst ourselves on the section and I start to pack up to go home. Sandra's brown-nosed friend wanders over and starts twittering.

'Are you alright?'

'No.' I say without looking at her.

'Sandra's really upset...'

'Well so am I.'

'I don't think she meant to...'

'I'm not interested, I'm going home.' And I leave.

Ann phones me later also trying to smooth things out. 'Look, you know what she's like, why don't you go and see her on Monday and sort it out. You know she likes you really...' I'm having none of it.

'Ann, you must be joking, there's no way I am apologising to her, and no way I am going to see her. She owes me an apology, and it's up to her to come to me.'

The weekend passed uncomfortably, and Monday comes and goes. No sign of Sandra coming to see me or calling me. Ann tries to persuade me to make the first move but I am steadfast. There is no way in the world I am easing her path. Don't get me wrong, I am the first to apologise if I think I have upset someone, even if I think I may be right. I hate a bad atmosphere and tension. It makes me anxious, but there are some times when I am not going to make the first move and this is definitely one of them. Had I complained about her behaviour she could have face disciplinary offences, and however much she hates me for using the rules to keep my work-life balance happy, I have done nothing wrong. Allowing her personal feelings to overflow through her mouth is inexcusable for me.

Tuesday arrives and around eleven my phone rings. It's Sandra. 'I think we need to chat. Will you come and see me. I want to apologise.'

I go to see her and she apologises for her behaviour. She tells me she has not slept all weekend worrying. (I am glad.) She tells me that she really likes me and thinks I am very intelligent. (Yeh, yeh) and we have a chat. I accept her apology and we pretend to be best friends. Right on cue Ann arrives into Sandra's office.

Ann has a great many strengths. She is enthusiastic, funny and is often up to no good! A real trickster, she would have been head of the escape committee in Colditz. Never short of a cunning plan, she could teach Blackadder a thing or two. Essentially though Ann is kind and has a big heart.

Like us all, she also has a few weaknesses, and although she is always first with an idea of how to implement any new initiative or directive the government delivers on a seemingly daily basis, patience is not one of her strong points. Ann, will rarely, if ever, wait and see, she will always be 'proactive!'

Our old boss Terry, whom I have known all my working life, was quite the opposite, and would always wait and see, react at the last minute and occasionally not act at all. This would infuriate Ann and often the office would come to a dead stop as we felt the floor vibrate as Ann marched down to Terry's room to give him what for. I am much more of a wait and see person. My experience of the civil service is that most often, if you leave something for a while, it will either change, or disappear never to be heard of again, to be replaced by yet another good idea from some young university graduate working in the department for ridiculous acronyms. Terry and I used to while away a few tax-payers minutes thinking up acronyms and ideas, some of which were brilliant! We wanted to invent a whole department of ACRONYMS. We even had various acronyms for the acronym, acronym! Well we would wouldn't we, we were civil servants!

To name a few in our time, we once had an influx of guidance for dealing with new age travellers and therefore we had a guide to NAT's, with not a can of fly spray in sight.

When they brought out a new Fraud Officers Guide they were going to call it 'the FOG' but decided they couldn't call it FOG, (that would make FOG user's sound silly!) so they called it FIG, and changed our job title to suit so we all became Fraud Investigators. I'd like to say we really didn't give a FIG what it was called, but I'm sure someone earned a promotion thinking up its politically correct title. The civil service was well ahead of the WAG's!

Years ago, the Vietnamese boat people came, bringing forth a whole plethora of new names for us to enjoy. My personal favourite was always Tang-the-Dong. Sorry Tang if that's you but I had hours of pleasure dealing with your claim, and we never knew whether to file you under 'Tang' or 'Dong'

Not that we didn't have a few of our own English ones. Plenty of Victoria Cross's, a smattering of Tina Salmon's, some 'P.Green's', but my favourite English one was of a mother and daughter. Mom married a "Mr Cotton" and she became "Polly Cotton," then, with a wonderful humour, (or cruel joke) she had a daughter and called her "Polly Esther Cotton." I bet she got lots of needle for that at school!

Some had more imaginative names such as Tuesday Sunrise, or Eastern Promise. Parents with eternal optimism.

Still, to make sure we never got too complacent, the government made sure that things were always changing. The labour exchange was replaced by the UBO, the UBO became the job centre and then because we got so good and professional we became jobcentre plus, and achieved 'agency' status! Well how clever were we, although no-one really had a clue what that meant!

Then at some point they decided we should dump our own clothes and all staff meeting the public were told they had to wear a uniform. Lots of controversy there and the union came out fighting, but eventually uniforms were worn.

...Until...

...The budget was cut, we ran out of money, and amazingly uniforms were scrapped!

Still, unperturbed, Sickness Benefit became Incapacity Benefit. Supplementary Benefit became Income Support but that was too easy so they split it into Jobseekers Allowance for working age and Minimum Income Guarantee, (MIG) for pensioners. Not to be confused with the MIG guide, which was the Managers Information Guide. Not sure what it advised them, but it was definitely not for pensioners!

As time progressed and the titles of the codes became too much for everyone we developed our own easy to use language of 'blue books' for blue folders, and 'yellow books' for the yellow folders. So much easier!

Ah, life was so much easier when I first joined and we had something called the 'A' code.

It all went pear-shaped when Income support was introduced. ENP's (Exceptional Need Payments for people with some urgent exceptional need) became Single Payments and the days of our ability to examine people's underwear in situ were over! Our pleasure of ordering cheap and nasty beds was also gone along with the claimants' pleasure from their ability to move from Supplementary Benefit to Sickness Benefit caused by a bad back from the cheap and nasty bed we'd delivered. It all became a thing of the past.

One day a man went into an office unemployed, wanting to claim benefit. He became really cross and managed somehow to get his arm trapped in the counter flap as the receptionist closed it. He came in unemployed and went out claiming sickness benefit! Having understood it was his own misdemeanour that had caused his circumstances to change, he didn't dare complain. Those were the days before personal injury compensation.

It was all so much more enjoyable before we became professional and someone had a bright idea to run our 'agency' as a 'business.' What a joke! They'll be expecting us to make a profit next, and what fun the shareholders meetings would be!

They started off by changing our 'claimants' into 'customers', and made us all wear name badges, that wasn't too bad though because we didn't have to use our own name if we didn't want to, which was a good idea if you upset someone since if they complained, no-one in the office knew who the hell they were referring to!

Eventually, we were dragged kicking and screaming into some sort of wobbly line and we all got a bit more serious about it.

Common-sense was replaced with self-appraisal, self-development plans, computers, e-mail, e-learning, e-tablets, (well even the customers had to evolve from alcohol, LSD and meth's) along with risk-assessments, risk management, but definitely no risk-taking!

Which brings me back to the story. After a few weeks, things have calmed down a bit but it leaves a nasty taste in the mouth and so after unrelenting nagging from Donna, she manages to inveigle her way into my chair and I find myself doing the most miserable boring job in the world. Security checking. I am not sure how it happens but it does. Ann has been bored stiff doing a spell at security checking. She tries to convince me that Sandra will get off my back if we change places and nags and nags eventually wheedling her way into us swapping jobs. Still, I only work twenty-five hours a week so I try to make the best of it.

I am given three days training by someone who used to work for me and who is definitely not my best friend, and am left with a code of instructions and a computer for company.

It is the most boring job ever, and I soon realise Ann has pulled a flanker. I make the best of it for a while, but with everything that has happened it all gets too much, I am utterly miserable and feel quite depressed. My happy working environment has all gone. I feel like I've hit a brick wall and I eventually go off sick. The doctor is really sympathetic and gives me a note for a month, tells me not to sit at home and suggests that writing things down can be very therapeutic, even if I throw it away afterwards. Wise words!

It's nearly the end of October and the hotel season ends in a few weeks. I ask the doctor if it would be o.k. to go away for a few days, and he tells me it would do me good. So, a flight booked and I pop off to Italy for a few days.

It is at the end of this week that I decide to go home and start to write. I have had quite a lot of time to think and reflect on things. I consider Jacqueline's nagging and the suggestion from the doctor and decide I will buy myself a lap-top when I go home and start to write things down. Hopefully it will clear my head and put things in order for me. Maybe Ann has done me a favour after all?

MORE TRAUMA!

I have a relaxing few days away, and feel clearer minded when I get back. I buy a new lap-top computer and start writing. Words spill out onto the screen and I am amazed at the things that I write. I discover that writing and talking are different. With writing you have to set the scene so that the reader is there with you. I also find that some of the words I use are so different from the spoken word.

I return to work and sometime later Sandra moves on to pastures new. Hurrah! A new manager arrives and he is really lovely. After some time he calls me into his room and asks me if I want to go and work in the jobcentre across the road for a while. It is a new initiative to try and get sick people back to work. I won't bore you with why or how, but I do it. I am really quite enjoying it all when it all comes to a grinding halt. In my absence, the security checking is being done by the person who trained me.

The next part of the story is a bit of a blur. Partly because I wasn't privy to what started it off or who exactly was involved, and more importantly what was going on behind my back. The next I know I am being informed, by my nice new boss, that I am being investigated. He knows no more than that and has been told only to tell me there is an investigation going on. I am shocked!

I try to carry on as the days turn into weeks and I hear nothing. Every now and again I ask him if he has heard anything and he says no. He checks to confirm things are still ongoing, and they are. Weeks turn into months and still I am no wiser. All the time I am becoming more and more stressed. I have worked out that it is involved with the security checking, and I am now doing yet another job. Eventually it all gets too much for me and I call in the in-house counselling service, 'Care First.' We are entitled to six sessions free of charge, the aim being to see if we can be kept at work

225

rather than going sick. After the second session I am in tears. The lady tells me that I am not coping and that to try and remain at work with this threat of disciplinary action hanging over me, is clearly impossible. She basically tells me to go sick.

I am reluctant since I think that the action will be suspended whilst I am off sick. She suggests I ask my doctor to write a letter saying I will not be fit for work until the disciplinary action is dealt with. It has been just over six months since I was first told about it and it has clearly taken its toll on my health.

I relent and tell her as she is leaving that I will phone my manager and tell him I am going sick. She leaves me in the office we are in and I call Richard, my boss. He is not at his desk, and by now I am feeling distraught. I phone Jacqueline and ask her to come up to me. She does and after finding Richard, I go home.

Next day I go to see the doctor, tell him what has happened and he gives me a note for a month. He also writes me a letter stating that until the matter is resolved I will not be fit for work. I post it off, and within a week receive a phone call stating that the investigation is almost complete and they will be able to send the allegations to me. (How thoughtful!)

Another few days goes by and I receive two more phone calls telling me it is all ready but is still with the typist which means that if it is posted it might not get to me until next week, so would it be all right to deliver it personally. (How kind!)

It is now April, Dino is staying with me and arrives back home half an hour before the district manager, who I am going to call Bill Bastardly. (Remember similar from Whacky Races.) I manage to contact Jane and she arrives onto the drive literally seconds before Bill Bastardly. Determined that I will not invite him in or thank him for his 'present' I open the door to his smug face. Just as he hands it over, Jane walks past. Clearly surprised to see her, he politely says, 'Oh, hello Jane!'

'Hello Dick.' She replies.

Next thing Dino walks behind me. 'Everything o.k. Gilly?' he asks.

'Yes thank you.' I reply.

Dick looks slightly uncomfortable and confused and says, 'Well I had better be off.'

I manage somehow not to thank him, or ease his discomfiture, and close the door.

We go into the lounge and open the package. It seems to revolve around allegations that I have not done certain checks. Nothing mind blowing seems to be involved and for the first time in months, I feel a little easier.

To cut another boring tale short, there are four particular allegations. I have explanations for all of them.

One of them involves checks not done for a period of some months. My answer, I wasn't actually doing the job at that time!

Second, is that I did two checks that conflict. My answer, I was asked to! To clarify, I obtain a witness statement as evidence, confirming I had brought it to Sandra's attention at a meeting that the two checks conflicted, and she said she would take responsibility for it as I was the only person in the office who knew how to do the second check.

Next is that one check that had not been performed at all. My answer, I was never asked to do it, had never seen it and had no knowledge of it. To clarify I point out that having read up on this check, I discover that Sandra was required to do a follow on check which had she done so, would have identified any error on my part. She has failed to do it.

I also point out that nothing was mentioned in my appraisal, and no checks had been made after I had been trained to support me or check that I was doing the job properly. I also point out that my training was woefully inadequate. (Having done some research I realise that I should have had much better training.)

Armed with my defence, weeks later, I am summoned to a 'fact-finding interview.' I have had one of these years before, funnily enough Dick was behind it all then, and failed spectacularly to prove anything then. I am starting to believe there is something personal involved with this.

Terry, my old boss, offers to accompany me to the interview. I am cheered by this since he will be very unpopular with Dick for openly showing support for me. (Terry was my direct manager at the last debacle and refused to interview me on the grounds it was so unfair.)

I have my interview with Dick, who is assisted by another person, present my defence and leave. I find the fact that my accusers are also my judges very worrying and unfair. Are they realistically going to admit they've got it wrong? Doubtful!

Two weeks later and I receive a written warning through the post. No explanation, no comments and clearly my evidence had been completely ignored. I am amazed.

A few days later and Richard phones. He has been told that the matter has been resolved and wonders when I am returning to work. I point out that it hasn't been resolved. He is surprised. 'I was told you had been sent a letter.'

'Yes, I have received a written warning through the post, but I am going to appeal. My doctor wrote a letter stating that until the matter was resolved I wouldn't be fit for work. As far as I'm concerned, the matter is not resolved so I won't be back until after an appeal.' I hear the dread in his voice as he has to go and report back and I can imagine lots of swearing from Bill Bastardly!

I prepare for an appeal. By now I am worn out with it all. The problem is that it fills every waking moment of my day. It doesn't matter where I am, what time of the day, or what I am doing, it hangs over me like a lead weight. I remain in touch with Ann from time to time but I am feeling mentally and emotionally exhausted.

A few more weeks pass and I have a date for my appeal. I feel a little more hopeful since my case is to be heard by an area manager. I have met her several times over the years and she has always struck me as down to earth and fair-minded. I hope I am right.

I get to my appeal supported by my regional trade union rep. I don't think he really understands the charges against me but his presence is reassuring.

We start the interview and after a while I get my opportunity to speak. By now I have almost lost the ability to go through all the allegations again. I give a brief account of my side of the allegations and then I speak from my heart and explain that although I am aware that mistakes can happen, I have no idea how I have found myself in the position I am in, and that I have not done anything knowingly wrong. After twenty something years of loyal service I am devastated. I find it difficult to keep control and start blubbing.

She is very kind. She asks if I can leave it with her for a while to look at. She also asks if she can have access to my appraisal reports. I tell her she can have access to whatever she wishes.

A week or so later and a letter arrives on the doorstep. I make a cup of tea, and open it nervously.

I am exonerated!

It states a list of management errors. Management failed in this, management failed in that and management failed in the other. I am elated. The best failure is my appraisal, where Sandra had written a note on my report thanking me for doing the checks I had been accused of conflicting with others!

It is the fifteenth of September 2003. I book an appointment to see the doctor and have great pleasure in telling him I have won, cleared my name, and thank him for his support. He gives me a note to return to work a week on Monday. I need a few days to catch up with myself. He also reminds me, as he has all the way through, that I need to change my job.

Returning home, head a little clearer I remember I owe my next door neighbour £1.60 for some hardware they got for me a few weeks ago. (They own a hardware shop and got me some catches for my wardrobe.) Although they have told me not to bother, I insist on paying so that if I want anything in the future, I won't be afraid to ask. Feeling happier than I have in weeks I go round to pay my debt and share my news.

As I leave their house, the man who lives next door to them is just walking past. He exchanges a joke and I walk out to the footpath. He starts chatting to me and we walk the few yards to the corner of the street. We continue to chat, I tell him about my job, and we get chatting about health and safety at work. And we chat…and we chat… and we chat…and I get colder, and colder, and colder!

Eventually I invite him for a gin and tonic, and show him the different layout of my bungalow to his. I explain I thought about buying the bungalow he now lives in, but hadn't sold my previous house in time. He tells me he has sold it and is hoping to move in a few weeks. His name is Graham.

A WEEK AWAY

During the time Dino and Filippo stayed with me, they extend many an invitation to go and stay with them "in their 'ome."

To be honest we didn't desire so many invitations, since the first one was enough to have our bags packed and ready for a week in the sun, hopefully at mainly their expense. Still, we keep the suitcase well covered and play it cool.

I still have the looming threat of the disciplinary hanging over me, but Jane and I make plans to travel to where the boys live. It's just along the coast from Sorrento around a twenty minute car journey although due to southern Italy traffic it usually takes at least an hour!

We book our flights and Dino makes arrangements to collect us from the airport and find us somewhere to stay. Before we know it, we are sipping a G&T on the plane and looking forward to a break together.

Jane and I have been friends for twenty years but as she has children, we have never been able to go away together. Her children are now grown up and we are excited about a girly break together.

We arrive in Napoli, and Dino is there to meet us. He puts our cases in his car and we head off. He tells us we are staying in Filippo's apartment as his parents are away in Sicily at their holiday home.

We are dropped off and told they will be back later to cook a meal for us. We can hardly wait!

We wander around and next thing Filippo appears, full of life and bounce, seemingly thrilled to see us. He shows us to his parents' room and says we can sleep here. He then shows us around the apartment and leaves us to shower and change.

The apartment was originally two and has been knocked into one. It is quite dark, and typical of Italian homes, has lots of ornate woodwork. It is also filled with

231

lots of artefacts, many of which are damaged making the whole effect quite spooky.

We know the reason they are damaged is as a consequence of the last earthquake in the area. Both Filippo and Dino's parents lost their homes and many possessions and the remnants are generally damaged. There are two items that are particularly disturbing. One is a small porcelain doll in a Moses basket that sits in the 'best-but-little-used' living room. The thing is we don't know what's in the basket until we peer in, and then the doll is so life-like it looks like a dead baby and scares the living daylights out of us!

The other, which gives Jane nightmares, is on top of a tall display cabinet outside the parents' bedroom, where Jane sleeps. (I move to the next room as the street noise keeps me awake.) It is an alabaster statue of a bleeding Madonna looking pretty miserable, and is made even worse by virtue of the fact that due to earthquake damage she has broken her fingers and nose. Draped in a rosary and gazing down at you as you walk past, in the middle of the night in the half light, she emits a ghostly aura and Jane always hurries past with a shiver.

Our first evening arrives and the boys arrive with their girlfriends. Their parents own a mozzarella factory and we are honoured with a feast of buffalo mozzarella served with basil and tomatoes. Mmm, yum, yum!

Well, it would have been, but you can get too much of a good thing, and we definitely do. Clearly Jane and I are ignorant to the finer points of lashings of buffalo mozzarella, because we both find it rather tasteless, especially when there are not enough juicy ripe tomatoes to flavour it.

However, being brought up to be polite we 'Mmm' and 'Ahh' in the right places and clear our plates...

...only to be presented with more!

As politely as we can we tell them how full we are and manage to stop the buffalo charging away with our calories!

Next morning Jane is up early, and I am up late. In fact, Jane is always up early and I am always up late!

Filippo is at work but has excelled himself and left some fresh pastries for us for breakfast. We eat and get ready to go out, and then wait.

This is another thing we learn to become accustomed to… waiting… We have been given no key to the apartment so we are unable to go out as we can't get back in. Without Rapunzel to lend us her hair, we are confined to our Ivory tower until we are met and accompanied.

Still, we remain blissfully ignorant of this for a couple of days and are happy to go wherever we are taken… as long as it's the beach! Dino calls for us and with suitable attire we go to the beach. It's a place called Seiano, a few miles along the coast.

When I say beach Jane redefines this by observing a few days later that the Italians get a load of hardcore, dump it in the sea, and call it a beach! That may sound a bit harsh, but effectively it's true. They may have lots of mountains, old bridges and Roman bath's in Italy, but on this coast, they 'aint got beaches like we have in England!

Anyway, we take two sun-beds and make ourselves comfortable soaking up the sun. Dino becomes a bit hyperactive and starts to show off his tan and body to the local females. Stretching and strutting about, he eventually takes himself off into the sea for a dip. A while later just as Jane and I are getting comfortable we are summoned into the sea.

Now, bearing in mind that we are on the Med, so no tides to worry about, our sun-beds are very close to the water, no more than ten feet, you wouldn't see any real problem for us getting from sun-bed to sea would you?

233

Wrong! I have a problem. I have the most sensitive feet in the whole world, not just the northern hemisphere, I mean, the whole world, and this means that ten feet takes longer to negotiate than ten miles with walking shoes. Added to this I am only six months recovered from my dislocated kneecap and you can see we have a problem. Jane is very patient, but does her usual trick and laughs at me! We decide the easiest way to get me to the sea is to walk into the sea in my shoes and then throw them back towards the sun-beds.

Sorted!

Once in the sea and I am able to become sleek and elegant as I swim about in the warm water. We follow Dino, around a large stone jetty and find ourselves a couple of hundred yards along the shore. Dino starts to make his way out of the water and summons us to follow as he has something to show us.

Problem again. I can't walk on the stones. Even worse, I can't even stand up in the water to even attempt to walk. My leg is still very weak and having been effectively weightless being in the water, getting to stand up and feel heavy again, I find I am unable to lift myself up. I have absolutely no strength in my legs and the more I try the worse I become! Jane starts to laugh, (no change there,) and I join in. Dino turns to see where we are and clearly unimpressed by two old women cavorting in the water, looks disgusted. This just makes us worse and despite Jane's best efforts to haul me up, it's no good. I can't move!

So, here I am in my hour of need. Helpless female needs strong burly man to come to rescue. Optimism runs high as the beach is covered with Latin ego's bursting to escape and impress Latin ladies who are bronzing nonchalantly, draped elegantly in designer beachwear.

Optimism soon turns to realisation that it 'aint gonna happen! Clearly beached English whale doesn't have the same appeal, but the problem remains that I'm stuck. Jane can't move me and Dino has disappeared.

Eventually a very kind Italian lady comes into the water and helps to haul me out. Of, course the nearer to the shore we get the heavier I feel and the more the stones hurt my feet. We have also attracted an audience of onlookers. Somehow, we manage to get out of the water and very gingerly make our way across to relative safety. The beach isn't very big and at the edge is a concrete walkway. Dino magically appears and ushers us along to a plunge pool. Trying to convince us to jump into the 'natural hot spring water' we are wary. His grin lets him down and we suspect the water is from a 'natural very icy cold spring.' We are right to be wary, but as the weather is so hot, I literally take the plunge! Very cold, very bracing and with nothing to hurt my feet, very quick to get out again!

Recovering my composure, we wander back to our sun-beds. Another treacherous trek across the rubble and I collapse exhausted onto my bed for a rest. A bite to eat and a good slosh of water and I recover well. Later in the day I brave the sea again, but make sure I come back the same way I go in. So much easier!

Eventually, the sun starts to go down and we make our way back. As we are dropped off we are told to be ready in a couple of hours to go out to eat. (Hope the buffalos are on holiday!)

We get ready and wait... again. This starts to become a problem as Jane spends ages doing her hair, and just when her hair is ready to go out, the boys are not. An hour later and her hair is no longer ready to go out, although our chariot has arrived and we are off. We spend an inordinate amount of time driving around, gathering the girls, and then head off to eat.

Next day and Dino arrives to take us out again. Filippo has furnished us with more pastries and we head off to another beach.

Today, we are taken somewhere Jane and I find spectacular. It's a beach, but not as we know it! First we are driven along the coast. Then we get on a boat and next thing we are out on the water. After around twenty

235

minutes, we arrive at a jetty at the bottom of some very steep cliffs, disembark and the boat disappears.

Looking up perched precariously clinging to the stony cliffs is a bar and restaurant.

Below, we are among lots of Italian people enjoying the sun. This time though at least the beach is natural. A mixture of shingle and rocks, we find a place to perch and enjoy the sun, sea and view.

The water is beautifully clear, and we take a dip before we are taken up to the restaurant for lunch. As we relax and enjoy the moment, we watch a group of people having fun with napkins. One of the group puts his napkin on his head and says something about English people. We laugh and I explain that the English tie a knot in four corners. After some good humour is exchanged we return to our food.

We choose a sea-food pasta dish and garlic bread, washed down with a couple of beers. It melts in the mouth and I can't remember tasting such soft, sweet, seafood.

We go back to sit in the sun for a while and then we make ready to leave. We are a bit surprised to be going so early but Dino looks triumphant. He tells us he is taking us somewhere very special.

'Beach?' says Jane. This becomes one of the few words in her vocabulary this week in a similar vein to 'drink!' appears in Father Ted!

'Yes, yes' replies Dino, but first I take you to a special place. Jane looks disappointed!

But, to be fair, we sit in our chariot like a pair of old ladies on a charabanc trip, and watch the world go by. Abandoning all responsibility for everything except hair and clothes we enjoy the sense of freedom we have.

We wend our way along the coast, stopping now and again for a picturesque view and find our journey's end winding down a very steep road heading down to the sea.

We are in Positano.

As anyone who has any knowledge of Positano, it really is a most beautiful village enveloped by steep cliffs looking out to sea. A favoured resort for romantic holidays and honeymooners, it is really quaint.

With a big grin on his face, Dino spreads his arms and tells us to go explore.

Jane and I exchange glances, a bit confused. Dino enlightens us by telling us that the shops here are 'world famooos' for the linen they sell. Finest quality there is!

Jane and I exchange glances again, and head off into the nearest shop. Dino watches us eagerly!

'Ooo! How lovely' says Jane looking at a cutwork linen dress in bright yellow.

'Absolutely beautiful!' I add.

Dino looks satisfied we are impressed and wanders away.

'Bloody horrible' Jane murmurs smiling at me. 'We could be on the beach!'

'Yes, I am agree with you.' I say (stealing one of Filippo's phrases.)

'Looks like we have to be really impressed and then we can go!'

Yep! Sounds good to me.'

Wandering in and out of the shops we try and look interested. To be honest, the linen really is lovely. Unfortunately there are a few 'buts'. First everything is phenomenally expensive. Secondly it all looks so old fashioned, unless you are around five foot ten and stick thin, and thirdly neither of us are keen on linen, and I have to point out that at this time in history, linen is not fashionable which makes it even less desirable.

Interspersed, between the clothes shops are lots of table linen shops, again very beautiful and much more desirable but without a mortgage, really expensive. The other shops sell Limoncello and a type of highly glazed and colourfully decorated kitchenware, along with wine jugs and the like which are equally expensive.

Every time we come out of a shop Dino looks at us expectantly. Have we bought anything? We make a great fuss of being confused by all the choice and unsure what to choose.

At one point we come out of a shop and find Dino talking on his mobile phone. He is talking to Filippo and telling him how much we are enjoying Positano! We don't disillusion him!

Eventually, we find ourselves on the beach edge. Picture-postcard beautiful, there are a few bars and a couple of huts selling things that look much more like the sort of thing we can get away with buying. Positano's version of kiss-me-quick hats and Blackpool trinkets, although there's no comparison, Jane wanders into one of them and I follow.

Jane decides to but a straw hat for her mother...

...Jane's mum is ninety years old...

...I buy a decorated tile with a house number on...

...I suspect my purchase may have more use...

Jane agrees!

Gushing with pleasure at our purchases we go across to meet Dino who has ordered us a drink to cool us down. I am not sure if it is to cool our excitement or the summer heat.

This is definitely worth the trip though as sitting here is so peaceful and away from it all I find it quite emotional. For no particular reason, I feel tears welling up in my eyes and vacate to the nearest loo to pull myself together. (Even the loos are posh!)

We finish our drinks and head off back to the car.

Now bearing in mind we have spent a few hours on a beach this morning, and Jane and I are always ignorant of any plans unless we are told, (which is rare) we are dressed in bikinis, no make-up, scary hair, beach shoes, shorts and a loose top to cover up.

We are definitely not in any way dressed to go out to eat in a posh restaurant. And the only reference to being dressed to kill, is in terms of Jane and I being so ill-informed of the next plan, our hosts are later in danger of being strangled.

So, for now, we are driven back in the direction from whence we came, in splendid ignorance. We stop at the now familiar home of the two girlfriends where they join us.

We head off again in two cars. By now it is getting dark, and we find out we are going to eat. We ask about going back to change, since the girls looks smart and gorgeous, but we are told there is no time. No time! We've had all day pithering around Positano, and now, we have no time to change!

Oh well, we have little choice but to go with the flow. It seems to take ages before we arrive at a trattoria type of restaurant somewhere up a mountain. As we go further up the mountain, the temperature drops, and Jane and I get cold. With nothing to wrap up in we are starting to shiver.

After a while we are shown to a table (outside of course!) and given menus. We start to realise that this is a favourite restaurant of the boys. The girls however are in playful mood and things are about to heat up! Whilst we are choosing, the boys are talking to the waitress and the girls start to giggle.

Meanwhile, there are two tables near us. One to the side of us already has occupants, and soon the other table behind us is occupied by a group of people.

The boys are starting to get irritable although Jane and I are ignorant as to why. The more irritated they become the more the girls giggle. The atmosphere starts to get a little tense, and despite the temperature in the group rising, Jane and I are still cold. As we start to shiver we whisper between ourselves and discuss the possibility of putting one of the tablecloths around our shoulders as a shawl. Eventually, after much deliberation, our order is taken and our food arrives. By now the boys are boiling and are making grumbling noises at the girls. Jane and I pick up that the girls are laughing at the waitress who apparently has a speech

239

impediment and a strange accent. For no particular reason other than to lighten things up a little, I decide to pick up a napkin, tie four knots in the corners and put it on my head. Wrong move! This seems to tip the boys over the edge. Dino looks evil, and Filippo loses all sense of fun in a split second. Glowering at me, he tells me I am being very disrespectful!

I am somewhere between seeing red and laughing hysterically. 'Disrespectful! How dare you. After the way you behaved in England and you always telling me that you didn't care a bit about respect in my country, I don't know how you have the nerve to call me disrespectful. In any case, at the restaurant we were in earlier, the clients were all sitting with napkins on their heads.'

'Well this restaurant is very elegant, and those people on the table behind are very important people.'

'It didn't bother you in England.'

Leaning across the table looking at me very seriously he says, 'Gill-e, in your country they just put you in jail. In Italy they kill you!' He gives me a knowing look as he nods towards the table behind us.

Choking on my beer I start to laugh, 'Blimey I didn't know you could be killed for wearing a napkin on your head!' Jane joins in, and the girls can't contain themselves. We are all laughing and the boys are furious!

We eat our food in relative silence. The second course arrives, the boys won't speak to any of us, and we behave like naughty schoolgirls. All of a sudden a lady off the table beside us picks up a tablecloth and wraps it around her shoulders.

Jane and I look at each other and smile. I can't help myself, I lean towards Filippo and say, 'you better tell her to take that off before she gets her head blown off!'

He turns a shade of puce and ignores me!

Eventually, the trial of the meal ends and we get back into the cars for the journey home. Dino is not speaking to his girlfriend, and isn't really sure whether to be cross with Jane and me. He seems more cross with his girlfriend so we get off lightly.

Dropping us at Filippo's apartment, Jane and I make a cup of tea, have a good titter and go to bed.

Next morning, we have no breakfast! No pastries and nothing in the fridge apart from a piece of parmesan which is welded to the back of it in three inches of ice. Looks like the peace is shattered!

Dino arrives to take us out again. He doesn't seem to be cross with us. Another day, another beach! Jane is happy.

We travel along the coast and stop at the top of a cliff. Looking over the edge it is a bit precarious. (Maybe it is punishment for yesterday. Refusal to buy linen and giggling in unseemly manner in restaurant!)

Dino has everything prepared. Two cool-bags full of food and water, and our beach towels. Sharing the load, we climb over a wall and start down a steep and winding narrow path. Now I know I am sounding like a bit of a winger, but as I have said, I have only been off crutches for a few weeks, and my left leg is quite weak. Add to this the psychosomatic fear of my kneecap popping out again, and I am like a ninety year old tottering gingerly along. Eventually we reach a break in the path. As we look down there is a big drop to the floor. Dino bids us to follow him as he negotiates his way across the gap by jumping. Jane and I are horrified, but there is no time to protest as he tells us to get a move on. We somehow manage to cross the abyss without falling or injuring ourselves and eventually arrive on a proper, nature made, shingle beach.

Trudging across the shingles we find a nice spot near a cave. Dino puts the bags inside the cave to keep cool and we settle ourselves down for a rest and a snooze.

Half an hour or so later, we are getting hot. We have a drink of water and wander towards the sea. I keep my shoes on to walk to the sea and then decide to leave them on whilst I get into the water. The problem then is that I realise they float and I find it impossible to keep upright as my shoes act like buoyancy aids on my feet and tip me head first down into the water. Eventually I have to discard them and throw them back onto the shore. The water is lovely, clean, cool and gentle, and with the beach being so awkward to get to there aren't many people on it. We swim for ages, and then decide to go back for another snooze. I crawl out on my hands and knees and Jane brings my shoes to me.

We return to our towels and lie in the sun. Dino feeds us with lovely ham and cheese cobs, some savouries, and then presents his ultimate gastronomic delight… 'Spaghetti cake!'

'I have stay up very late to make this for you last night' he says beaming at us.

'Looks lovely.' Jane says, a little too enthusiastically.

He cuts us a slice. Jane takes a few bites and asks for the recipe. Basically it looks a bit like a quiche but is made with spaghetti, which has been boiled to death and squashed into a flan dish, mixed with a few tomatoes and an egg poured over the top. Looks and feels extremely heavy.

I take a small bite and want to vomit!

Jane senses my anguish and asks Dino for some water. He gets up to go into the cave and quick as a flash, Jane grabs my cake, complete with tin foil and flings it hard and back, up and over her shoulder. The cake has vanished! Fortunately there is a ledge just above and behind us and we can only assume it landed there. We don't go to check, just in case it landed somewhere it shouldn't, like some unfortunate person's lap!

Dino tries to tempt us with more but we tell him we are more than satisfied with our feast, and the water is more than sufficient for us!

As we rest and digest our food, we survey the beach. We spot a man lying flat out on the stones. He has no towel to lie on and seems to fidget quite a lot. This is unsurprising as the stones are burning hot even to touch with our hands. They are impossible to walk on, (not just for me either!) and he doesn't have anything to lie on. We watch transfixed as to how he can lie there. Eventually he gets up, walks to the sea and goes for a swim. Coming back he lies face down on the stones and fidgets some more. Another twenty minutes pass by and he goes to swim again and back to the beach face up again.

We are getting hot again and wander down to the water for a dip to cool down. After a swim, we walk back up the beach, and I can no longer contain my curiosity. I walk to him and ask him in my best Italian how he can lie there and not burn. He tells me that three years ago he was diagnosed with terminal cancer and given just a few weeks to live. He was untreatable. He decided to take himself off into the woods and started to eat herbs and live off the land. Every day he would come to the beach to take the sun and then go into the water to cleanse. He believed the combination of herbs, heat, and cleansing would cure him. He said he spent twenty minutes on his front and the same on his back three times, and went to swim in between each movement, even in winter. His cancer is now cured. There is no trace of it in his body, and he believes this is the secret to his new and healthy existence.

Almost as amazing as his story, is that I understand him, and as he doesn't speak a word of English! I feel very pleased with myself.

As the sun starts to drop, we pack up and begin the long trek back up the slope and back to the apartment.

We are told to be ready in a couple of hours and then we go off to eat. No temper tantrums this time and we have a nice evening in a pizzeria.

Next morning and still no breakfast. Seems the novelty has definitely worn off. Filippo works during the daytimes. He has studied law at university and has

243

gained some work experience in a law firm so is unable to join us during the daytime. (Bliss!)

Today we go to a different beach again. Not as nice as the others but we still get the sun. Every day Dino asks us if we want to do anything else, and we always say no. He tells us about all the lovely places to go, but other than a bit of shopping we just want to relax and soak up the sun. He tries to tempt us into visiting Pompeii in the evening which he says is lit up beautifully. We reply with if he wants to go there in the evenings we are happy to go, but by the end of the week we haven't seen Pompeii by day or night.

This evening we are going to a party. It is at the house of some relatives/friends of the girlfriends. We are told to be ready by eight thirty, and we are. By nine o'clock, Jane's hair is ready to go out, and by nine thirty we are glowing in the evening heat. By ten, we are ready for bed, and at ten fifteen they all arrive and ask us if we are ready as we are late!

We learn as the week progresses that we have two time zones. English time, which is that we are ready by the time stated, and Italian time, which is any time you like, but never 'on time'.

Apparently even by their standards they are late. There was an emergency in the mozzarella factory, (maybe the buffalo ran off with the cheese?) and they have spent all evening preparing food for a party.

We arrive at a house somewhere and pull up outside a large pair of metal gates. The gates open and we drive in.

The house is magnificent, and the gardens spectacular. The whole thing seems slightly surreal, and I can hardly remember being there as it was all so out of context. We are treated like honoured guests and fed and watered copiously. Photos are taken, so we can prove we were there, and mid-way through the evening I go to check out the bathroom. It is like walking through a stately home. High, ornately decorated ceilings, huge rooms and the loo is unbelievable. Very grand and posh. Even Buck House would be proud of it!

Eventually we are dragged away and go to bed late having spent a very enjoyable evening.

Next day and its back to our favourite beach, the first one we visited where I entertained the audience on the beach. More careful this time and we spend a pleasant few hours topping up the tan. Dino likes to leave us and wanders about strutting his stuff and puffing up his chest to the local girls. He also seems to be getting a little irritated that Jane and I are developing tan's that are starting to rival his!

Later, we return to our ivory tower and wait. Tonight we are treated to homemade bolognese, and then we go to a bar on the beach. We spend a lovely night, as having a drink on the beach is really pleasant with the cool breeze washing across our sun heated skin. We return to the apartment relatively early pleased to have an early night.

During this week a few patterns have developed.

Jane's hair is never ready to go out on time. Sometimes it's too early but usually it is much too late.

We are always ready to go out on time and our hosts never are.

We wait patiently and just as we are getting so tired that we are ready to go to bed, they turn up and take us out!

We are asked daily if we want to go to see Pompeii by night, but are never taken there, and apart from when we go to the beach, we are rarely properly attired or prepared for any trip we go on, mainly because we are told we are going to do one thing and then end up doing something completely different.

One such happening is towards the end of our stay. Unusually we have made a request and asked if we can go and do a bit of shopping. Jane particularly, wants to get a few bits and pieces for her family. After around three days of asking and being assured that we will have plenty of opportunity for shopping, we are no nearer to

245

seeing any shops than fly to the moon. We pass loads of them, but never stop to go and browse. We start to get a bit twitchy. Added to which we have both been bitten quite badly by mosquito's and have no antihistamine to help. Again, despite various requests we are no closer to seeing a pharmacy. Jane gets bitten before me, very rare as I am a mosquito magnet, her bites are numerous and her feet begin to swell. My bites are soon catching up and by the time we eventually do get to a pharmacy, my feet are so swollen an elephant would have looked more elegant in a pair of stilettos than me.

Anyway, this evening we are told we are going to go for a late night swim in Sorrento. Jane and I are a bit dubious, but we are assured it's loads of fun and to be ready early. We will eat later. As ever, we are ready and waiting. We are wearing our bikini's covered by shorts and a t-shirt. No make-up or hair done, after all we are going for a swim aren't we?

Wrong!

We start off blind to our ignorance, but start to smell a rat when we pick up Dino's girlfriend. She looks gorgeous in a red sleeveless polo-neck jumper, hair beautiful and make-up applied. Nothing is said probably because she hasn't a clue we believe we are going swimming.

We arrive in Sorrento, and Filippo and his girlfriend join us. She also looks lovely, and the boys are equally smart-casual. We ask about going swimming, and they look at us as though we are barmy! They then deny any knowledge that we were to go swimming and proceed to take us shopping!

Shopping? Shopping? Who on earth mentioned bloody shopping? We were told we were going swimming! We are rendered speechless!

Walking through the streets of Sorrento, Dino eventually asks us if we want to buy anything. Resisting the urge to strangle and disembowel him there and then, we point out that although there are lots of things we would like to purchase, having believed we were going swimming, we didn't bring any money or cards with us. How stupid are we!

They treat us to an ice-cream (how generous!) and at last get to a pharmacy for some anti-histamine and then we head back. To say we are peeved would be an understatement, but we wait until the next day before we make our feelings known and insist we are taken shopping, today!

Our determination pays off and we are allowed to go shopping and even better, we are joined by Filippo's girlfriend, who shows us to all the shops we desire. We are fortunate in that everything is cheaper than in England, and because of the time of year, there are sales everywhere and we pick up some bargains.

Happy with our purchases we take them back to the apartment before heading to the beach!

This evening we are off to a party. We are under strict instructions as to how to behave. Filippo is like a bear with a sore behind and spends ages telling us how important these people are. We are going to the "'ome of 'iz boss.' It is a birthday party, and even better it is festival season so lots of fireworks will be going off around us. It is imperative we give a good impression as his whole career and life depend on it! No tablecloths or napkins allowed!

We get the message and try not to wind him up. (Very hard!)

For once we are all ready to go out at the same time, including Jane's hair. I am wearing an Armani animal print stretchy dress, and Jane is wearing a hand-printed Escada dress. With our newly acquired tan, and hours spent in the gym we don't look half bad.

Dino arrives to pick us up and we are treated to another lecture about how to behave in polite company. Patience is wearing thin, and we ask some deliberately obtuse questions to keep them on their toes.

We arrive at an apartment building and are soon being welcomed as honoured English guests. After a few drinks and some food, we relax a little. Jane spends ages

247

talking to a man who appears to be the village idiot. Oh well, maybe he's more interesting than he looks.

Meantime I am having fun with a group of people who end up in a circle doing some kind of hokey-cokey. Everyone is enjoying themselves and the man who is host, (Filippo's boss) makes a big fuss of me.

Later in the evening and we watch a spectacle of light as half an hour of fireworks goes off. This is quite a regular event in Italy as various festivals throughout the year are celebrated communally. We tell the story of Guy Fawkes, whom no-one has ever heard of, (in fact every time I have told any Italians about Guy Fawkes they have never heard of him!) and even Filippo can't claim that they have a better one of those in Italy.

After the fireworks a birthday cake is presented and we all sing 'Happy Birthday.' The guests love to hear Jane and me singing it in English, and out of nowhere a man appears with a guitar and we start singing. Attention turns to the three of us as we sing all sorts of tunes from the Beatles to James Taylor and lots in between. Our guitarist loves English music and we entertain the crowd for half an hour or so.

Before we know it and it is time to go. We bid farewell to our new friends and are shown out by Filippo's boss and his sister, who has been a wonderful hostess filling our glasses as well as our plates, although she doesn't seem to smile much.

We get into the car and de-briefing begins.

I ask Jane why she spent so long talking to the village idiot.

'What do you mean?' she asks

'That bloke you were talking to for ages.' I reply.

'Oh him, well I thought I'd try and impress him.'

'Why?'

'Well, he's Pippo's boss.'

'No he isn't.'

'He is.'

248

'He isn't!'

A moment passes, and Jane leans forward. 'Pippo, was that your boss I was talking to with the glasses and clowns clothes?'

'No, he's just a junior clerk'

'Bugger! You mean to tell me I sat talking to that idiot for an hour trying to impress him on your behalf and he's just a clerk, why didn't you tell me?'

'I thought you liked him.'

Jane looks choked, and for a change I am the one laughing.

'Well, at least I got the right one to impress' I say, 'His boss was the man I was chatting to and dancing with. He was very pleasant. And what about his sister she was a good hostess, but she looked a bit miserable. She never seemed to smile.'

'What sister?' Jane says.

'The lady who was doing everything, she showed us out when we left.'

'That wasn't his sister.'

'It was. You remember she came to the door with us, dark hair and quite a lot older looking then him.'

'That wasn't his sister, it was his wife!'

'Naaa, he wasn't married, it was his sister.'

Leaning forward I ask Filippo, 'Was that woman who showed us out your boss's sister?'

'No it was his wife.'

'Oops!' this time Jane starts to laugh!

Ah well, on the basis of kill or cure, we have at least made an impression. Everyone seemed to make a fuss of us and we used all our English grace and charm politely and cordially. Filippo didn't seem to notice anything untoward, and for now his position at the firm seems secure!

On the way back we stop at an off licence and pick up a bottle of Prosecco to celebrate. We sit on the balcony for a while when we get back and unusually Pippo is friendly and chatty.

Next day and we realise that soon we will be at the end of our week away. Jane comes into my room with a cup of tea. We chat for a while and she says, 'I don't know how you sleep in here.'

'Why?'

'Well, it must be really uncomfortable on that bed.'

'It's a bit uncomfortable I must admit.'

'Well why don't you make the bed up?'

'It is made up. This is it, mind you I must admit, I am surprised that the bedding is in such a poor state. It looks like they've turned this sheet sides to middle.'

'But this is just a dust cover, the bedding is over there.' She says pointing to a beautiful pile of crisp linen on top of a chest of drawers.

'Damn! I can't believe I've spent nearly a whole week on a bloody dust sheet!'

Jane laughs, (just for a change) and helps me make up my bed.

As we are soon to go home we are invited to Dino's parents' home for a meal. We are to be the honoured guests and there will be lots of family there.

We arrive early evening and are met like old friends by Dino's mum, dad and brother. He is younger than Dino and more sensitive and serious. With not a hair out of place and attire just so, he is perfectly presented.

We are taken on a tour of the house. It is on three storeys and used to be a warehouse. Like many other families they had to relocate after their home was destroyed in the earthquake. After our tour, we go to the basement and out into a courtyard garden. The table is set and Dino's girlfriend and his sister are helping his mum with the food preparation. We are given a glass of chilled Limoncello and wait for the other guests to arrive.

By the time we eat there are around sixteen of us including Dino's uncle and his wife, (my Italian teacher Lucio's, dad).

So, quite a crowd! I sit next to Lucio's dad. He speaks around twelve languages including Russian and Chinese, so English is no problem. He does however sound quite intimidating since he had an operation that damaged his vocal cords and now speaks with a horse-like whisper. Very much as you would expect an Italian godfather! We chat for some time and then I move around the group.

I start to chat to Dino's dad. He speaks no English at all, but is so enthusiastic to talk to me he speaks at a hundred miles an hour and I find it really difficult to keep up. He does speak a little bit of French, which Jane speaks, but even she can't keep up so we resort to Italian with me translating for Jane. To be fair, I manage to keep up with him really well, but occasionally lose the thread. Jane says 'what did he say' and I reply with a wide smile 'Ahh, haven't a clue!' We both laugh and nod and we carry on where we left off.

We share a lovely evening, good food, convivial company and the rhythmic song of the crickets to break any silences. Towards the end of the evening, the family raise a glass or two towards Jane and myself, we all promise to keep in touch, (Jane and I need only one invitation!) and we make to leave. Lucio's dad asks me if we have been into Sorrento. I tell him we went one evening but didn't get chance to do any shopping! I tell him I would really like to buy a wooden marquetry picture. Many years ago I had one but it disappeared over several house moves. He asks me if I know the Lucky Store. 'Ah yes, that's the place I remember. It was over twenty years ago but I remember it well. There was beautiful furniture in there and every manner of wooden artefacts.'

'I used to own it.' He replies.

'Really?'

'Yes, I set it up and was in partnership, but I sold out some time ago. Go in there, and choose what you like and tell them you know me.'

'Yes, yes I will. We just need Dino to take us there and we only have one day left.'

'Dino' he says, 'take Gillian and Jane to the lucky store and tell them I sent you, yes?'

'Yes Uncle.'

'You take them tomorrow.'

'Yes Uncle.'

And he does! (He's probably frightened not to!)

I choose a hand cut picture depicting the bay of Sorrento. It is one of the most expensive pictures they have, but I love it. Jane has picked up a couple of trinkets along the way. We go to pay and we are given a huge discount as Dino introduces us and himself. Happy with our booty, we also get a chance to go and do some other shopping in Sorrento! If only we had met Uncle, earlier!

Nearly time for our departure and the boys have one more trick up their sleeve. They take us to the local water spa.

If anyone has ever visited Bath and tasted the water there, they will have an idea of what I am about to describe. For those who haven't, imagine the worst smell in the world, (partner's body gases included!) double it, and multiply it twenty times. That's where we are taken.

The locals come from miles away on Sundays and are allowed to take as much of these healing waters as they can carry. There is a big queue and eventually following one's nose we end up in a huge room full of taps. Each tap produces a different 'flavour' of water. I use the term flavour very loosely. Fermented egg water would be a more gentle term. A cow shed full of heifers on a diet of baked beans would be closer. We are tortured and bullied to 'taste' each of the water's and told how each of them is therapeutic for any particular ailment.

Ailment! I prefer to keep my ailment thanks! In fact I'll take on some extras if it means I don't have to drink this stuff! I am not particularly tickled stomached, and I'll try anything once, but having tried it once the

252

other nineteen are an unnecessary form of torture. Even Jane is struggling to smile through this one!

We eventually escape through a hole in the fence and after tunnelling for a few days reach the safety of Switzerland. (Just joking!)

In fact, we leave in a hasty manner and head for the hills! Actually this is nearer the truth as we go from the spa to a vantage point locally and are able to see all across the bay of Naples. We take a few photographs, my elephant feet in sharp focus, and go for lunch.

Back to the apartment and Jane and I pack to prepare to go home.

We spend the evening at a pizzeria and go back fairly early. A final night passes and before we know it we are back on the plane to Coventry airport. Tired and tanned, but relaxed and happy. We have a bite to eat and a cup of tea, and doze our way home.

GRAHAM

During the time that Dino was staying with me, I decided to have some work done to increase my wardrobe space for my large clothes collection. I remember one day Jane-the-masseuse telling me she had just bought a new item of clothing and wasn't sure what to discard. I was confused! She said well one-in, one-out! I had never considered this procedure. Mine is invariably, another one in, another one in! When there is no more room, get another wardrobe! She laughed at my reaction... and I did the same!

However, I still had too many clothes and not enough wardrobe space. I had two wardrobes in the loft, and changed my summer and winter wear with the changing seasons.

So I asked a man who was working on my neighbours' property to build me some wardrobes. To cut a long story short, he made a real mess of them, part of which resulted in the doors not closing properly.

Talking to my neighbour one day, I told him what a mess it all was and showed him. He said, 'Well I can get you some of those catches,' (he runs a hardware shop) next day he brought them round.

'How much do I owe you?' I asked.

'Nothing' he replied.

'No, I must pay you otherwise I won't be able to ask for anything else.'

'Well, it's £1.60, drop it in whenever you like.' And with that he was gone.

Every time I went out I reminded myself to go round and pay, but in the event it was around 8 weeks before I went round.

Handing over my debt, we have a chat and I tell them my news that I have just received my letter from work exonerating me from all the allegations made, and I am returning to work on Monday.

I then make to leave.

As I stand on the doorstep, a man is walking past. He calls to the lady, 'fancy a walk?' I recognise him as Graham, he lives next door to them, and as their bungalow is on the corner, my garden touches his at the corner. I remember him from the summer when we had a chat over the neighbour's fence.

'You must be joking, I wouldn't walk anywhere with you!' she replies, smiling.

They exchange some banter, and I use this moment to walk away.

Reaching the pavement, he starts chatting.

'How are you?' he asks.

'Fine' I reply, 'I'm really pleased, because I've received a letter from work this morning, clearing me from all those allegations they made against me.'

'Great, are you going back to work then?'

'Yes, but I'm having another week off sick first, to relax. It's been so stressful, I could do with a few weeks to get over it all really, but I'll have to make do with a week!'

We reach the corner of the street and continue chatting.

'I love your suit' he says.

'Thank you' I reply

'No, really, it looks lovely, the way it's cut is really classy.'

'Thanks,' I reply, (I am starting to like him more and more!!)

After standing on the corner for what seems like ages I am starting to get cold, but he keeps me talking and I turn my back to the draught that is blowing up over the fields and through my suit, in an attempt to keep warm. We discuss work, health and safety, (he really knows how to charm, I hear you cry!) and lots of things in between, including the layout of our respective bungalows.

Although identical in layout, the bungalows have been renovated and restyled over the years, and mine and Graham's are now different in some respects. I spy an opportunity to get warm, and invite him for a look round and share a gin and tonic.

'…or are you on your way somewhere?' I ask

'No, I was just out for a walk, I'd love to see your bungalow, and share a G&T.'

We sit in the kitchen and chat for a while, during which the conversation turns to my trees.

I have a very small garden, and just three leylandii trees for privacy. The effect is that my garden is entirely private and allows me to wander naked around it, if I so wish, with no chance of anyone seeing me. The only thing is the trees grow!

'I need to chop them down a bit.' I confess.

'Do you want a hand? I would be happy to do them for you. I like doing bits and pieces, any time you need a hand, just ask me.'

'That would be great, are you sure you don't mind?'

'It would be a pleasure' he says, smiling. 'How about tomorrow?'

'That would be lovely.'

'Right, well I'd better go, let me know when you're ready and I'll come round. See you tomorrow. I'll bring a bottle of wine!'

'Ok, bye.'

He leaves, and I go round to Jane's to help her with the curtains we are making for her lounge. They are really big and heavy, buckram lined, and definitely easier with two sets of hands. We muse over another cottage industry potential we could branch out into, and I tell her I am freezing, having spent about three quarters of an hour on the corner talking to Graham, but that I am getting my trees cut down as recompense.

We chat about this and that, make good progress with the expanse of fabric, and then after a coffee I go home.

Next day, and I am off for my Italian lesson with Lucio in the morning, and then to an M.S Roadshow with Christine in the afternoon. I remember that Graham

257

is due be coming round. I see him outside his house as I am leaving in the afternoon, and stop the car.

'Hiya, sorry, but I forgot, I am off to an M.S Roadshow with my sister this afternoon, could we change the day for the trees?'

'Yes, no problem. What about tomorrow?'

'Fine, but I go to church in the morning, is the afternoon ok?

'Yep, I'm in all day. Just knock the door when you're ready. I like your boots!'

All the time I am talking to him, I can see he is trying not to look at my legs. I am wearing a pair of long black leather boots, and another suit, very sexy and gypsy like, with a skirt that is full length, but cut into panels. Sitting down it falls into a split that shows my thigh. I try discretely to keep it pulled together.

'Are you sure? I'm sorry to mess you about. If you'd rather leave it until another time...'

'...Tomorrow's fine, just knock the door when you're ready.'

'Thanks a lot. Bye.'

'See ya!'

Sunday arrives, and on the way back from church I knock his door and tell him I am home. He picks up a bottle of wine for my approval and a few minutes later he arrives armed with plenty of bags and some tools.

He proceeds to chop down my three trees during which he enlists the help of the man who lives behind me, who brings his shredder. The job is done really quickly and bags are filled. It's great, it takes me all day normally to chop my trees and at the end I'm knackered!

I know he lives alone, and so have bought some steak to cook as a way of a thank you. As he finishes I offer to cook and he offers to go out to eat. Whilst we decide what to do we open the wine and share a glass together. Eventually, Graham persuades me that it is easier to go out, and it saves me cooking he says.

He goes home for a quick bath and change. I change and throw on a pair of jeans and a blouse. I walk to his house and we go off to the local Cantonese restaurant just five minutes away in his purple Ford ka.

The restaurant is almost empty, just one other couple for the most part, and Graham and I sit chatting. He is easy to talk to, intelligent, and good company. We have a bottle of wine, which I drink the majority of as he is driving and around 10.30pm we go home. I invite him for a coffee at my house and he accepts. We then sit chatting until very late into the night. I tell him a bit about myself and that I do reflexology. He asks me to look at his feet which I do, and then he asks if he can look at mine! He holds my foot gently in his hand for ages, during which we carry on talking like old friends. I explain that I am very content with my life, have many friends, travel a lot and live a very full and active life. I explain that I have become very content living alone and am quite happy in my own company. He tells me he has been living alone for three and a half years, and he too is very happy living alone and being in his own company. Eventually at around 2.30am, he kneels down on the floor next to me and kisses me. He slides his hand under my blouse and as his hand touches my skin, he says 'I love you.'

I am taken aback, but it is obvious it was out of his mouth before his brain was in gear, and so I don't respond.

'Can we go to bed?' he asks.

'Ok, but I don't want to mislead you. Graham, I can tell you about tonight, but I can't tell you about tomorrow. Is that ok?'

'Yes, that's fine, can we go to bed?'

'Ok.'

We walk to my bedroom and get into bed...

...We don't really get out again for two days!!!

We spend the most fantastic night ever together. He is the most wonderful and sensitive lover I have ever known. We just sort of "fit together."

Around 4.45am I ask him what time he has to go to work.

'6.00am!'

'I don't want you to go.' I say.

'I won't go then!' he replies.

'Really?'

'Really!'

At 6.30am, when he calls into work sick.

He has an animated conversation with one of his colleagues about the fact that he is sick and has a bad stomach, after which he tells me he has never taken a day off work unless he has been very poorly, during all his working life.We are both very tired, but content. Sleepily we cuddle up together and as he holds me in his arms, he asks me;

'You will still be here when I wake up won't you?' His eyes look really searching.

'Yes, I'll still be here.'

'Promise?'

'Promise.' And with that we fall asleep for a few hours.

We spend the day sleeping, making love, and eating the steak I bought the day before. All the time he is so gentle and kind. I think he's a really nice man, but I am not sure I want to get involved. The other thing is, my chin! It's been shredded. Graham has a really strong beard and is really hairy, (except his head! Must be all that testosterone!) During the time we have spent together, his beard has turned into a porcupine coat and my chin has been its victim! It is really sore and weeping. Very quickly it forms a large scab, from which I cannot hide!

At the end of the day we return to bed and again as we cuddle up together, Graham asks me 'you will be here in the morning won't you?'

'Yes,' I reply, 'I'll be here...'

Next morning Graham goes to work, and I go out and about, whilst trying to hide my chin! I call my sister and tell her all about my last two days.

260

'So, what's he like then?' she asks.

'He's lovely, really kind and gentle, I don't fancy him though.'

'Oh yeah!'

'No, really. I don't fancy him, and I don't want to hurt him, he's far too nice. I think he's really going to fall for me though.'

'So, let me get this right. You have just spent the last two days in bed, you're seeing him tonight, you haven't stopped talking about him, but you don't fancy him!'

'Well, yeah, like I say, he's so lovely, but I'm quite happy on my own…'

'…give him two weeks then tell me you don't fancy him.'

Later in the day and I go shopping, arriving home there is a bunch of flowers outside my front door. They are perfect, wrapped in brown paper, and tied with a raffia bow, they look beautiful. Full of autumn colours, with a sunflower in the middle, there is a note, 'Love Graham x.' I smile to myself as I take them inside.

By now it's Wednesday, and I have to collect Christine from the hospital after some steroid treatment. She has three days of out-patient treatment, and I have to collect her each day.

When I tell Graham what I am doing he says 'call in to where I work on the way if you like.'

Telling Christine, we decide to call in to Graham's workplace, we wait on the car park and he comes out to meet us. Chris gets out of the car, and wobbling and smiling meets Graham. After we leave, she says, 'he's lovely, definitely give him two weeks and then tell me you don't fancy him!'

In the evening, he asks me if I will go with him to see the new house he is buying. It is just down the road, and he is waiting to exchange contracts.

I wander around to his house, and after going to see the new house we go back to his bungalow where we listen to some music, share a bottle of wine, and spend another lovely night together. This time we stay at his house, and watch another of the beautiful sunsets we are so lucky to have displayed for us by the Lord's watercolours.

During the last few days, Graham has done most of the talking. I behave in a way most unlike me, in that I say very little!

Basically, I have become so content with my life generally I decide that if anyone is going to come into my life, they have to prove they have something to offer me. This sounds a bit callous, but there's an element of self-preservation involved. During the last few years, I have learned how to be happy in my own company. I am independent, and my territory, i.e. my home is safe and protected. Whilst I have been travelling, I have always had home to return to, safe and sound. No-one to bother me if I so choose, and this is the first time I have been 'invaded,' or rather allowed anyone into my personal space. I feel slightly vulnerable, in that Graham 'knows' my neighbours, and that means my privacy is under threat. The other thing is that I am genuinely happy with my life, and I really do want to know that Graham can make it even better.

To say I make life difficult for him is an understatement, and by the end of two weeks, I am amazed he hasn't given up and gone home. Another thing I also find unnerving is that he keeps saying things that I think. Some of which I have written in my book! How does he know! He doesn't know anyone who has read it, (there are only a few people who have read bits of it,) and I am amazed at his words. The first one that strikes me, is when we are talking about freedom, he says 'you can hold a bird in your hand, but when you let it go, it will fly away. Keep your hand open and it can return of its own free will. I can't believe he says this!

Another thing he says is 'no-one can make you happy. You can only make yourself happy, and then you can be happy with other people.' (He's pinching my lines!)

262

The more time I spend with him the more I become fascinated with him.

Thursday morning, and Graham goes off to work again. As he leaves, he asks me, 'Will you send me a text this morning?'

'Yes, Ok' I reply.

'Thanks.'

To be honest, I am a bit put out! What a cheek asking me to send him a text! That means he'll have my mobile phone number! Then the other side of me thinks, well to be honest, half the population has it, I argue with myself over the topic thinking, yes but that's because I gave it to them, has he tricked me into giving it to him? I smile at his cunning!

By 11.50am I still haven't sent him a text, but I know time is running out, and as I said I would text him, I feel obliged to keep my word.

...11.55am and I text him something fairly innocuous, which strangely I can't remember.

A few minutes later I receive a reply. It is lovely, and I feel as if I have been wrapped in a blanket. Very sweet, but not gushing, I am prompted to reply and we spend the day leisurely exchanging texts.

By Thursday evening, I am off to college. This term Jane-the-masseuse and I have decided to do a sports massage course. I bring her up to date with my goings on and discuss what I should do tonight. We agree I will go straight home. I have seen him every day since Sunday, and since I don't fancy him, think I'll have a night off!

We have a real laugh at college and leave around 8.30pm. I am really tired and look forward to a night at home.

However...!

...As I drive past Graham's bungalow, the car comes to a halt. I can't believe it, my foot has landed on the brake, and I am stopped outside. I send him a text.

'Where are you?'

'At home, where are you?'

'Outside your house.'

263

'The idea of your beautiful body floating past my window is a thought more beautiful than the most beautiful sunset.'

That was it! I am hooked!

I go in, we sit chatting, and he comes back with me... After that, he never goes home again...

...However, I am still not giving in too easily! I tell him what I think are all the bad things about me, things that I think if he is going to dislike, he can find out sooner rather than later, and then leave before I become attached to him too much.

He isn't put off, and keeps saying, 'Please just give me a chance.'

I tell him that I have male friends that I go out with sometimes...

'Great, no problem' he says.

I tell him some are ex boyfriends...

'Fine' he says.

'I go on holiday on my own to visit my friend Mario?'

'Great, when are you going?'

'Probably in the next three or four weeks?'

'Lovely, I'll take you to the airport if you like.'

'Are you sure about all this?'

'Of course, I think you are lovely, and I just want you to give me a chance.'

'Ok, but there's one more thing...'

'What?'

'I'm writing a book, well a cross between a book and a journal really...'

'What about?'

'My life. Well about the last two or three years of it to be specific, since I've been travelling alone. I've had a great time and my friend Jacqueline nagged me into writing it down, so I have.'

'Can I read it sometime?'

'Of course, if you'd like to.'

'I'd love to.'

Hmmmmm! Seems he's not going to be put off easily!

I decide to give him a chance, and during the next week or so we spend hours talking, and I tell him more about myself. Being with him is just so easy. We get on so well together and seem to have so many things in common. We share the same ideas and opinions on so many things it's like meeting my soul mate.

On the Sunday of our first week together, I tell him I am going to church.

'Can I come with you?'

'Well, yes if you want to. I go to a church in West Bromwich though.'

'How come?'

'Well, it's our parish church from when we were children, and my sister still lives there and goes to church there, so I go as well.'

'I have always gone to church, well on and off until we moved here. I made my children go until they were around fourteen and they were old enough to make their own decision about it. I went to a church in Tividale. It's closed now. I was a server, carried the cross, candles, everything!'

I can hardly believe it, he's a churchgoer as well!

We arrive at church, Graham in a suit, and me too. As soon as Christine sees him, she says, 'You scrub up quite well don't you!'

She has only seen him at his workplace, where he wears a uniform and is covered in oil, he laughs, and is then repeatedly asked by various members of the congregation who he is, and does he know what I'm like! Everyone is really friendly, and makes him welcome. The banter about me is good humoured, and he takes it all in good part. (Good job I had told him in advance, can't say he wasn't warned!)

During the second week he asks me if I would like to meet his children. They are both grown up with their own children, but he tells me he has never taken any of his past girlfriends to meet them before. A couple of friends had met them, but he has never introduced any girl formally. He says although his children are twenty seven and twenty nine, he never wanted to take girls to meet them, and more particularly his grandchildren, unless he was serious about them. Consequently I am the first.

His children are really nice to me, and welcome me kindly. It all seems so easy! In the first two weeks we have been inseparable, I have been completely honest with him about myself, we have met our respective families, and everything seems hunky-dory! I can't believe my luck! And of course, at the end of the two weeks, Christine asks me

'So do you fancy him then?'

'Yes, Ok, he's lovely.'

'Told you so!'

Typical sister! Always has to have the last word!

The next few weeks pass by as I return to work, but that's another story!

TRIAL BY DISTANCE

After a few weeks I decide to check out whether or not Graham is really prepared to allow me to flap my feathers. I am becoming increasingly fond of him and time spent with him is just so easy. We get on really well and he seems more than happy to embrace everything about me.

With his encouragement I book a flight to Italy and he takes me to the airport. Passing through passport control, I feel a pang of emotion as I watch him disappear from view. Already I know that this will be a difficult parting.

Graham is in the midst of selling his bungalow and I suggest, (and hope) that he stays in my bungalow whilst I am away. He says he will.

As soon as I land I call him and we text each other regularly as the few days I am away pass by.

I also receive a telephone call from Dino whilst I am there to inform me that he is coming back to stay with us for three months. He will be arriving in a couple of weeks and is hoping to study written English at Birmingham University. 'Is that o.k.?'

I call Graham and ask him if he has any objections. He says he is quite happy for him to come.

One evening I am getting ready to go down to dinner and I call him. I am ready apart from putting my dress on and am wearing my dressing gown.

We chat and chat, and chat and chat, and chat... Eventually there is a knock at my room door and as I open it Mario is standing there with a food trolley.

'We wondered where you are and your phone is busy. I assume you are talking to Graham?'

'Yes. Why?'

'Gillian it is almost ten o'clock and you have not eaten. I have brought you some food!'

'Oh, thanks, sorry!'

'No problem, enjoy your meal.'

Graham and I laugh and I eat and we continue chatting. Eventually we say goodnight. I am going home tomorrow and have missed him immensely. The phone timer shows we have been on the phone for 3hours, 33 minutes.

I really hope he has missed me too, and start to get nervous and excited about seeing him tomorrow afternoon. I also start to worry what he will think about my journal. I left it with him to read so that he has a good idea of what I have been up to for the last few years. I want to make sure he is willing to accept me as I am, warts and all. I hope very much that he will...

TWO LETTUCES AND A JAR OF MAYONNAISE

Dino arrives and as usual takes over the house. Graham is wonderful and easy going, and we all muddle around each other. Generally Graham and I sit in the kitchen talking and eating around the table. Dino spends his weekday evenings in his room studying or in the lounge watching TV.

Weekends take on a different routine. Friday evenings and Dino turns into some sort of excited gigolo. All the lights are on in the house, the walls shake as both the TV and CD player are competing for attention, aftershave fills the air and the wardrobe is brought to life as Dino prepares to go out! Eventually Graham insists on running him to the station (just to make sure he doesn't miss his train!) and peace returns for a day or so whilst Birmingham adjusts to its Italian tourist's testosterone!

A few weeks pass and my sister and I go to spend a few days with a friend in Great Yarmouth. I leave the boys at home together.

Although Great Yarmouth is not the other side of the world, it takes such a long time to get there and the mobile phone signal is so wonky, I feel an awfully long way away from Graham. I really miss him, and call him every evening. We chat as long as the signal permits before saying goodnight.

Arriving home I am really excited to see him again and we chat as though we have been apart for weeks!

I ask how he has got on with Dino. Graham tells me fine except that he can't understand his lack of common-sense.

'Do you know what he did yesterday?' he asks me.

'No, what?'

'Well, we had run out of milk and mayonnaise. I told him in the morning and asked him to bring some back with him and do you know what he did?' He says, his voice rising.

'No, do tell!'

'He came home with two lettuces! Can you believe it! We've run out of milk and mayonnaise and he comes home with two lettuces! Then guess what he does?'

'Go on'

'He stands there, chops them up and starts eating them! I can't believe it. And then he asks me if I want some! Unbelievable!'

'What did you say?'

'I said no thanks, I'd rather have a cup of tea but we haven't got any milk and you can't make a decent cup of tea with lettuces! Bloody idiot!'

I start to laugh and Graham joins in. He then replays the tale to anyone who stands still long enough to listen for weeks to come!

NOVEMBER IN PARIS

I can't actually remember exactly when Graham proposed to me, but I can remember that we were in bed, (typical!) and it was very soon after we got together.

'Will you marry me?'

'Pardon?' (I heard the first time, but wanted to make the moment last a bit longer!)

'Will you marry me?'

'Ask me next year, and I'll think about it.' I say kissing him and smiling.

Over the next few weeks, he asks me again, and I eventually say 'Yes, but only if you promise to give up smoking!'

'Ok, it's a deal.'

And so, very quickly we are getting engaged.

As soon as I say 'yes' Graham takes me shopping, and we go to the local well-respected jewellers in Stourbridge. I try on lots of rings, and we narrow it down to two. A single square set solitaire, and a three stone ring. (Two diamond and centre sapphire.) We decide on the solitaire, but go away to think about it first.

We return later and buy it. It has to go away to be sized, and in between times we decide we want to go away for a few days to celebrate our engagement. We want to go somewhere neither of us has been before, and it comes down to a choice between Paris or one of the Canaries. We choose Paris.

We set off for Luton airport early in the morning, before all the traffic, and arrive in plenty of time. Before we know it, we are hurtling down the runway, and this time I am holding hands with my future husband. Arriving at Paris airport, we collect our luggage and head off to the station. Very soon we arrive at Gard du Nord. It's huge!

After successfully purchasing tickets we try to find the platform. No chance! I ask for directions and despite understanding fairly well the French, we can't find it! Eventually whilst we study a map, a man approaches us.

'Can I 'elp you?' he says in a French accent.

'Oh thank you, we are trying to find the platform to Pigalle.'

'Ah, straight ahead, and you come to it. It is quite a long way though.

'Thank you so much, we are really grateful.'

'No problem, 'opefully someone will 'elp me if ever I am in England!'

'It would be a pleasure!'

We eventually arrive at the platform and the train arrives a few minutes later. As we travel along, we are both amazed at the amount of graffiti adorning the rail tunnels and stations, (and how on earth do they get it there?) We arrive at our destination, and having booked our hotel over the internet on the advice from Jane, emerge from the station into the daylight.

I am shocked!

We are in the middle of the red light district. I feel like a fish out of water and very vulnerable.

Graham has a big smile on his face, and offers to give me his credit card to go on a spending spree!

We cross the road to the hotel, and go inside. I have a very bad feeling about it all.

Graham fills in the forms and we are given a key to our room. Arriving inside our room doesn't do anything to make me feel better. About as big as a shoe box, it is definitely 'compact and bijoux!' The window overlooks an air conditioning unit and is about as grey and bleak as you can imagine. I am just trying to get over the shock, thinking maybe it might not be that bad, and then it gets worse. We open the bathroom door, and then close it again!

'We can't stay here.' Graham says.

'I'm really sorry Graham, I think I have booked us into the wrong hotel!'

'I thought it was an engagement present!' he says trying to make me feel better.

We have booked into one of a chain of hotels, and clearly are in the wrong place. Jane had described the hotel to us as being at the top of a hill in the shadow of Sacre Coeure. She had seen it when she came a few months ago. It was being refurbished and had watched new beds being delivered. Definitely not where we are right now!

We decide there is no way we can stay here, even if it means losing our deposit and moving somewhere else.

We go downstairs and speak to the receptionist. We get a blank response. Gray asks to speak to the manager, and a lady appears. She listens to our plight, and looks at my pallid face, as I stand there in my posh black coat burying my face in the big furry collar. I think she takes pity, and smiling says not to worry, it is a mistake that happens quite regularly. A call to the other hotel and we are transferred. She says it is just up the hill opposite, ten minutes walk, but with our luggage we take a taxi.

Arriving at our second hotel is a much better experience. Clean, friendly and the key to the room reveals a clean, recently redecorated and refurbished room. We have a window that has the most fantastic view over Paris you could imagine.

We can see the Eiffel tower and the Champs Elise beyond, and have a 180 degree vista of Paris and its sprawling suburbs stretching out as far as you can see. Things are starting to look much better.

We put our things away and go out to find a place to eat. We choose a small restaurant, and are shown to a table in the window. The seats are small bucket style seats and after the cold outdoors, and long early morning journey, followed by the trauma of finding our hotel, we feel snug and warm. We eat a steak in a red wine sauce, with veggies and a bottle of red wine. Towards the end of the meal, it all gets too much for Gray and he nods off! Secured in his bucket seat though, no one notices and after a gentle nudge, we pay the bill and go back to our room. We are both really exhausted, and decide to have a snooze...

...Fifteen hours later, we wake up! Blimey, we certainly know how to do the 'romance-in-style' thing, but we are happy together and eventually venture out to eat again.

We are there for five days, and I grant you November may not show Paris at its best, but we both dream of lying in the canaries somewhere, in the sun, by the pool, with a cool drink. Instead, we are wrapped up with layers of clothes, thermal gloves, hats, waterproofs, and rain spattered glasses. But we're in love so we gloss over it all and enjoy the arctic chill of the Eiffel Tower, and windy blast along the Seine, and as my Godmother always says, 'It all brings us closer together!' Well in this case we had to, for bodily warmth!

On the way back as we walk along the street towards the station, I see a huge pile of leaves underneath a tree. Swept up ready to be collected, I take a running jump and land knee high in the middle. I ask Gray to take a photograph as I pick up a huge pile and throw them into the air like confetti. Surprisingly he seems a bit reluctant, and I have to become quite insistent before he complies. Photo taken I ask him why he was hesitant, and he nods behind me. Two gendarme walking ten yards away are walking towards us. Oops! As they draw near they nod, smile and walk past. Phew!

Later on they prove to be very friendly and helpful as we try to find the station entrance to go back to Pigalle. (The station is 200 yards away from the one we arrived on, being a one-way exit.)

Another day and we can't face going into the city, and fighting with the railway station entrances so we wander up to Sacre Coeure, where we see the famous street painters. With my hair stuck to my face, and a big red nose, we choose a man to paint my portrait. I ask him to be kind to me, and I have to say he paints a beautiful picture of me, very natural, but not windswept!

Sunday, and this is the day we have decided to officially become engaged. We wander up to Sacre Coeure and into the huge cathedral at the top. It is absolutely heaving with people, and the hushed tones that emanate as they walk create a whoosh-whoosh sound like being in the middle of a forest with the wind blowing through the trees. The mass movement of the people move along like worker ants out foraging; all moving in exactly the same direction, and following the same path, no pushing and shoving, all beautifully well behaved and ordered. We find a quite seat just to the side of the moving walkway of people and sit down. We listen to the nuns singing their angelic song, bedecked in their black habits and crisp starched whiter than white toppings. We listen for a while and Graham turns to me and asks, 'Will you do me the greatest honour of becoming my wife?'

'It would be my pleasure.' I reply, and with that he slips my beautiful single stone diamond ring over the third finger of my left hand, and kisses me.

We stay awhile holding hands and listening to the music. It is amazing to imagine being so solitary in this place where there are hundreds of people passing by, but we are quite alone, and we both agree that being in one of the Lord's houses to make our first commitment was just exactly as it should be.

We return to our hotel, stopping off to have something to eat on the way. In the evening Graham has bought us tickets to go the Moulin Rouge. We are not sure what to expect, but I have brought a dress to wear. During the afternoon, we have a bath each, and while Graham is in the bath we sit chatting. We talk about my work, and all of a sudden, I start to cry uncontrollably. Graham gets out of the bath and standing together in our damp towels puts his arms around me and comforts me. Sitting me down he gently tells me it's time to make some decisions. 'You know how it is,' he says, 'I'm not going to tell you what to do. I'll give you all the options and you decide what you want to do. You know I'll support you, whatever you decide. The way I see it, you can either, carry on as you are, reduce your hours, apply for a transfer, any combination of the three, or leave. From my perspective, carrying on as you are is making you ill, and very unhappy?'

'Yes.'

Would reducing your hours staying there help?'

'No.'

'How about a transfer to a different office, would that help?'

'Not really, I still feel someone would be after me.'

'What about a different department?'

'Possibly, at least I would be away from the people who have done this to me.'

'And what about leaving?'

'Sounds wonderful, but I don't know if we can afford it.'

'Can we afford the effect on your health of you staying and being like this all the time?'

'No, I suppose not.'

'Right, well in your own time, you decide what you want to do, and I'll support you, you know that don't you.'

'Yes, thank you Gray.'

'Now, dry your eyes, I'm taking my fiancée to a show tonight, and she wants to look her best!'

An hour later and we outside the Moulin Rouge waiting to go inside. There are hundreds of people as we snake our way inside. On the way Graham tells me he has tried to book the best seats but to be honest he isn't sure as it was highly confusing on the web site! I tell him not to worry, I am sure it will be fine.

We are shown to our seats which are almost at the front, and find ourselves sitting opposite each other on a long table, side on to the middle of the stage. We are squashed in like sardines, arms pinned to our sides. There are two couples between us and the stage, but as we are so close together that equates to only two bum widths, and small ones at that!

We are given a choice of red or white wine and two choices for our three course meal, which is served with amazing dexterity, and are entertained by various singers to keep us relaxed. With definitely no room for straying elbows, we eat our meal, which considering the number of people to be served all at once, was not too bad. Meal over and plates are whisked away and we are served with champagne, a reward for us fledglings for managing to eat in nest-like cosiness without falling off our perch!

As we relax, a lady wanders around taking souvenir photographs of people, many of whom have extricated themselves to the flat stage at the side of us. For Graham and myself, this proves to be just too difficult, and the threat of sending our fellow companions reeling like falling dominoes keeps us in our seats and the lady takes our photo 'in situe.'

We chat to the couple immediately to my right and only one bum width from the stage. They are on holiday and have the same feeling of 'pile 'em high' that we have, and as we chat, someone comes along and tells the couple on the end, to 'keep your legs in.' then a stage suddenly hurtles towards us and stops when it joins our table. We are really at the front now and next thing the lights dim and the show begins...

...And what a show it is, absolutely spectacular from start to finish and goes at such a fantastic pace you really don't have time to catch your breath. Interspersed with solo acts which are equally fantastic, we are treated to an evening of true entertainment, lavish costuming and choreography. I don't think I will ever see anything like it again. Spellbound, and just as we think it can't get any more spectacular, the stage moves back and the floor opens up. A huge glass tank of water rises out filled with very large snakes. A beautiful young lady dives in and proceeds to dance with the snakes with such elegance and sophistication it renders us speechless! At the end the tank retreats, the stage returns and the audience applaud...

...And then it happens! All in slow motion, the man next to Graham is holding his glass of champagne, and then he isn't! Graham's elbow has strayed a millimetre too far and knocked the glass out of the American's hand!

Well, to be fair, Graham manages to rescue the glass before it lands, and deserves credit for this feat of reflexive dexterity, but this is short lived as the contents have escaped and are heading the American man's lap. Not even thunderbirds could perform this international rescue, and all too quickly the bubbly liquid has landed, inch perfect in his crutch and is dripping all down his trousers.

Graham and I exchange horrified glances and try to find something to soak it up with. The look on the man's face is not happy. We are so tightly packed his natural instinct to stand up is stifled, and the next instinct, to get a hankie out of his pocket is virtually impossible without the former! Graham, has however, managed to overcome all the odds and finds a hankie and starts trying to mop him up. Another bad mistake, as he discovers dabbing another man's crutch, even in this situation is not a welcome gesture! Apologies abound and the dampened man effuses 'no problem, don't worry,' type expressions which no-one believes. The whole incident seems completely in keeping with the evening, and keeps Graham and me highly amused for months to come.

The rest of the evening continues at the same captivating pace as before and all too soon the show is over. Marvellous!

We take a taxi back to the hotel and sharing a glass of wine, pour over the memories of our day. Opening the window we watch night-time Paris with its 'Mary- Poppins' type rooftops below us and we fully expect Dick-Van-Dyke to pop up at any moment singing chim-chimeny.

To our left The Eiffel Tower stands in all its glory, lit up like a Christmas tree, as the rest of the Parisian night lights twinkle in its shadow. The view from this window has made our trip to Paris worthwhile, but to be honest, although interspersed with highlights, we won't be rushing back.

Our days, fall into a regular pattern, we walk down to a delicatessen on the corner of the street just below the hotel, and buy breakfast. Then we wander to a café where we have a wonderful marshmallow-sweet milky hot chocolate. Then we walk a while, before lunching at a variety of hostelries, our favourite being a place that serve fantastic sausage, egg and chips, and then back to the hotel for a snooze before we start the evening tour for tea. Hard work, all those decisions, and we both become more and more exhausted, sleeping late and retiring early. However we get on really well together and enjoy being in one another's company.

One day on one of our walks we arrive at the top of a very long and steep set of steps running alongside a funicular. It has been raining and everywhere is wet. We start walking down and meet a lady coming up. To make space for her to get past, Graham steps onto the slope that forms the edge alongside the steps.

Whoosh!

He goes sliding down like 'Eddie the Eagle' on a bad day. Hurtling down the steps with him, I am running, as hand in hand, we nearly lose grip on each other and I see the shortest and most dramatic engagement coming to a sticky and embarrassing end! Spurred on by this humiliating thought, we make an almighty effort as Gray ends up on his bum, legs akimbo, but safe, sound and thankfully stopped!

The one thing that we do find really irritating though is the fact that some of the shopkeepers are quite rude. They spot us as English tourists and immediately refuse to understand any word of English. After a while I start speaking a mixture of broken French, and Italian with a French accent, and they instantly become much

279

friendlier except for the woman in the perfume shop down the road from the hotel. Every day we walk past this shop and the smell emanating from within is beautiful. Eventually we walk in and are greeted with the customary grunt. I ask her in every language I can think of, 'What is the beautiful smell?' She shrugs and grunts, in a language that anyone in the world could understand, that she doesn't know. Unperturbed we try some different perfumes before buying a bottle. The truth is we are determined to by something just to prove we are serious! Her face however doesn't flicker. Must be all that perfume really does get up your nose in the end!

Returning home Dino, Graham and Myself are invited to my sisters for an engagement dinner. Christine's partner cooks and selects a different wine for each course. After an aperitif of champagne and three courses, my head starts to swim! I head off to the loo to involuntarily say bye-bye to the food and liquid I have just consumed as my stomach is saying go away to its overloaded contents, and a few minutes later as I slide down the stairs, aided by my suede skirt, towards Graham's open arms as I implore him, 'Please don't take advantage of me!' Fat chance! Make up sliding down my face, hair like a bad advert for hair spray, and my stomach likely to involuntarily evacuate at any moment he helps me back upstairs and puts me into my sister's bed, wishes me good night and promises he is not angry with me. I promptly go to sleep and wake up next day to a pair of loving arms as he returns to fetch me.

A few weeks go by, and it is nearly Christmas. Dino decides after careful thought, to return home before Christmas. We have all got on so well, (apart from the odd lettuce that came between us!) Graham asks him to return for our wedding as a best man. He promises he will and is excited at the prospect. He offers to arrange our honeymoon if required and we promise to keep in touch regularly with one another. With a cheery wave at Birmingham Station, he heads off to Stansted, whilst Graham and I return home, alone. Wonderful! And to celebrate our new found freedom to be able to walk naked around the house again, we stop off on the way at a "Greasy-Lil's" café for a fry-up!

In the evening, the novelty of having the house to ourselves means we move from room to room not quite knowing where to go! We settle on the lounge, Gray starts off in the rocking chair. He has managed to reclaim his territory. He then joins me on the settee as we watch T.V for the first time in ages.

WORK AGAIN!

Since returning from Paris, work becomes more and more difficult. I come home exhausted and depressed. Some evenings I sit in the chair and have tears rolling down my face.

One day at work, I am given a message about the latest appraisal system. Delivered by e-learning, I am required to study it, digest it, and then implement it. I spend two days trying to access it on the computer since it is seemingly temperamental. Presumably I have to press the buttons without feeling cynical before it will work, I use a pen to press the computer keys to try to reduce cynical vibes travelling along my keypad and 'hey presto' it works and I am exposed to a new phenomenon for me. 'E-learning!'

Pressing all the buttons in the right order allows my machine to record my progress on a personal pie-chart (lucky me!) so that should I have to leave and exit for any reason, (such as watching some paint dry) I can return to the place I left. So now I also possess an 'E-book-page-marker.' Marvellous!

My eyes start to roll within seconds, and I retreat for a coffee. (Book marker in place, of course) Returning, my eyes roll again, as I find looking at the screen makes my head want to explode. Each time I try, the same thing happens. I start to worry, because even if I read the information over and over, I still don't get it. I find it impossible to retain or understand. I go and speak to a few other people about it. They all seem to have done it and agree it's a load of crap but don't seem to be in a panic over it. I decide it must be me, but try as I might, I just can't do it. The thing is I'm not very good at blagging this sort of thing. As long as I can understand the basics, I'm ok, but this may as well have been written in Chinese for all the use it is to me. I decide to give up for now and do something really useful. I go to the loo and then return to count my paperclips.

Graham becomes increasingly worried about me and one night it all comes to a head. I have collapsed into the settee crying and unable to move. I am already upset about having to go back to work on Monday. It's Thursday evening and work is three days away. We have plans for the weekend and I feel like the weekend has already gone before it has even started. He sits down with me, puts his arms round me and like a good Martian, (he has read the Mars-Venus book three times) reminds me of my options. I realise I don't fit in there anymore and am really unhappy. Since returning I have become paranoid that 'they' are after me again. I don't know when or how, but having won back my integrity, reputation and innocence, I believe it is only a matter of time before it all starts again.

Eventually, we decide. Give up work.

We discuss how and when, and decide that I will work until the end of January. With Christmas near which will give me a break along with the annual leave I have left, I can leave on the last day of January, with my last working day being the fifteenth of January. We consider my leaving sooner, but after nearly 25 years of service, I want time to get used to the idea and enjoy the pleasures of leaving.

I wait for a couple of weeks and sit at work each day watching and thinking, 'all this crap, soon it will all be a thing of the past.' I delete e-mails without reading them, and listen to all the bureaucratic bull-shit being delivered via post, mail and word of mouth all day, every day, thinking, yippee! Soon all this will be a distant memory! I tell my boss in advance one Thursday as I am going home that I am probably going to hand in my notice. I know he is planning staffing moves and after all the support he has given me I don't want to mislead him.

Returning on Monday with my letter, it seems everyone knows already! Bless him, he thought he could tell the supervisors and they would keep it a secret! I am annoyed that people have been told before I have

284

officially handed in my letter, but smile at his naivety that he still believes everyone else shares his integrity.

So with my resignation letter that spells the end of my working life as I know it, I hand it in.

During the next few days, people come to see me and ask if it's true. 'Yes', I reply happily, and feel that already I am detached from it all. It's like I'm no longer a member of the club. Not that people behave any differently towards me as such, but everything has an addendum attached to it. 'Oh it won't affect you will it because you're leaving,' or 'There's no point in telling you, you won't be here.'

It feels strange, but not euphoric. I am so happy to be leaving, but sad that this place has become so unpleasant for me. I have no doubt some of the cynics will be saying, 'Hmm, she has her meal ticket out of here. Met a man who will support her, got engaged, saw a way out and took it.' Well, I'm sorry to disappoint you folks, but it isn't like that at all. I was brought up to be independent and contribute your fair share. To give up my financial independence is a decision that has not been made lightly, or irreverently, or without careful thought. Exactly the same as my decision to marry Graham.

And so, the weeks go by until January the fifteenth approaches. Time drags. I am surprised. I thought that it would fly past, but it doesn't. I still feel paranoid, I still struggle to drag myself out of bed and I still feel exhausted at the end of each day as I wait for something terrible to happen as time for the last chance to get me ticks by.

Nothing happens, and ironically, I am moved to sit with a different group of people for my last few weeks after Christmas. It is such a relief. They are 'normal,' friendly and make me welcome. I actually start to think that if I had worked here when I came back I may not have handed my notice in. But then I realise that it wouldn't change things that much and as my paranoia is bubbling just below the surface my decision to go becomes more and more reinforced.

During the last couple of weeks, I relax a little and start to clear out my desk. I do it slowly, and savour every handful of paper that I deposit into the confidential waste sacks. My boss offers not to send me any more e-mails, but I ask him to keep sending them as I take great delight in looking at then, not understanding them and deleting them! He agrees and the highlight of my day, other than going home, is deleting my e-mails. In between training someone to do my job, and quietly confident that they baddies have given up on me, I also start to do naughty things! I browse the internet during works time just because I shouldn't. I use the telephone to make private calls and commit the ultimate sin by leaving my mobile phone switched on and visible on my desk! Good grief, I am amazed I am not frog-marched through the door into an armed response van. Of course most people have their phones on vibrate, but keep them out of sight. We are a professional organisation now and anything personal is left at the door, (including personalities please!) I also chat about things that aren't work related. Now that's really naughty. The week before I am leaving I am talking to the social fund supervisor, about my forthcoming wedding. She tells me her sister-in-law has a bridal shop nearby and is up the road from my hairdresser. 'I didn't know that!' I say.

'Well, I don't want you to feel pressurised into going there.' She replies.

'No, of course, but I will go and have a look when I'm passing.' I tell her.

Each day, Graham, makes me a lunch box and puts a love note inside. Each one counts down the days for me, and I love it. My last day arrives and he takes the day off work to take me and collect me later.

I am amazed at how many cards and gifts arrive on my desk. I have felt so isolated and so many of my friends have moved on I genuinely never expected anything like this. They have had a whip round and asked me what I would like. I am again surprised at how much has been collected, especially since there are so many people leaving just now, and I have never known so few staff in post. I ask for a dictionary, (what else!) and as people gather to present my gift, I am really happy. I tell them all I have waited for years, watching other people in this spot, wishing it was my turn... And now it is, it feels great!

A few of my closer friends and I go for a drink across the road and Graham joins us. He stays for an extra pint and arrives at my desk later in the afternoon. I am happy he is with me to hold my hand as we walk away together and into the wild blue yonder that is home. No stress, no threats, and a long lie in! Heavenly!

And that's it. Almost 25 years in Her Majesty's Service. Gone!

It is strange writing this, since very early on in this book, I wrote the following about the time when I had returned to work after being off sick, but before I knew an investigation had begun. How prophetic!

'...I return to my desk and don't quite know where to start. It's the end of the quarter and lots of checks to sign off with that piece of paper to sign to say you've done your job properly. Trouble is this piece of paper is hotter than the proverbial potato and will definitely be used against you when we see fit...'

Well, no more!

LIFE AFTER WORK

Next day, I spend all morning in bed. I think of it all going on without me, and go back to sleep. Graham tells me to sleep as much as I like and take my time. He says he thinks it will take me months before I start to feel better again. For the next few weeks I sleep a lot and try to remember I haven't got to go to work anymore. I am kept busy by two new Italians who have come to stay. I had made a commitment before I met Graham for Mario 'poco' to come over to stay and Graham is happy to honour my obligation. Also a friend of Dino arrives and they stay together living in the 'Little House' Graham bought when he met me which is just down the road. It soon becomes obvious that they have very different personalities and merely tolerate each other. They won't be keeping in touch on their return home!

Towards the end of January Christine and I go to the hairdresser. I browse through the latest glossy magazines and find a bridal magazine full of beautiful dresses, modelled by equally beautiful models! As we leave, I ask Christine if she has anything else to do. She says no, so I ask her if she fancies having a look in the bridal shop further along the road that my friend suggested. Although we haven't actually set the exact date, we know we want to get married this year. So off we go, and within an hour or so, I walk out with a wedding dress!

Well, not quite literally, I have chosen one and am advised in shocked tones that I have left it quite late!

'Late! It's still January!'

'Ah, but the dress is made in China and takes three months to arrive!'

Oh no. I am late! Having said that, I am not pressured in any way and the lady asks me if I want to go away and think about it or have a look elsewhere. I don't.

I know that almost all bridal dresses are beautiful, and have had enough of a struggle to choose this one. Any more choices will send my head into meltdown. I pick the one we all like best and stick to it. (I also avoid the palaver of, find a dress you like, spend hours travelling around lots of other shops, and come back to the first one you saw. Take my advice, cut out the stress and stick to your first idea!)

I had a few vague ideas about a dress. I didn't want to spend a fortune on something I will never wear again so thought about a sleek and elegant dress with a fish tail. Thinking I can have it altered to wear as an evening dress afterwards, it will be more practical. However, trying on dresses in the shop I am surprised that they are nowhere near as expensive as I had imagined. With this thought I end up going the whole hog. I choose an ivory full length dress, with a little bit of beading, and a long train. It is just off the shoulder, and has detachable voile sleeves. Perfect! Only thing is my weight! We 'um and ah' over what size to order, I have put on a stone since meeting Graham, we both have! My clothes are all too tight, so, time to get back to the gym and lose weight and tone up. We order a twelve!

As we come to pay, Christine gets her purse out. More rare than piggies with wings, she offers to pay for my dress. I am really touched and say 'yes, thank you' immediately! She only has a bit of cash, so we decide to go for something to eat and return with a deposit.

Afterwards, I phone Graham and tell him the news. 'I've got my wedding dress!'

'What?'

'I've got my dress!'

He is confused!

'..And Christine has paid for it!'

He really is confused, and is now convinced I am joking! The comment that Christine has paid is too much of a joke to be true!

'No, really, I have and she has.'

'Honestly?'

'Honestly.'

I think this is the first time he really knows we are getting married. He is so excited and overwhelmed he can hardly believe it.

Arriving home he has two bunches of flowers, one for me and one for Chrissy.

So now we have the dress, we only need, well, everything else. Including a date for getting married!

THE WEDDING

Graham and I spend some time trying to decide on a date. He works in industry so has the industrial fortnight at the end of July as a fixed holiday and we eventually decide that we should use this two week break as a honeymoon.

There are only a few problems to overcome, the first being a reception. Because we haven't booked years in advance, everywhere is booked. We are not tied to getting married on any particular day so decide Sunday may be better. We visit several local establishments and whichever way we look at the packages on offer, it seems it's going to be around fifty pounds a head. The thing is, if it didn't have the word 'Wedding' attached to it, we could probably knock thirty quid a head off straight away! One of the 'in' places to have the reception wants to charge us a pound a head extra for a linen napkin. We find this outrageous as their cheapest package starts at a reasonable thirty-eight pounds a head, but by the time the added extras like drinks, linen napkins, food, crockery, cutlery, (chairs and tables are included,) the cost is extortionate! Okay, so I have exaggerated slightly, (but not about the linen napkins!) but you get my drift. The only good thing is they are all available on our chosen day

Plan 'B' comes into operation. Do it ourselves.

We look around for various rooms and find a church hall nearby. Very nice. Modern with a clean kitchen and it is available. We check with our chef friend, he is available too. The cost is half of what we have been looking at and is looking good.

A few days later, we are talking to our next door neighbours. We tell them of our search for a reception venue and he suggests the golf club he is a member of. He says they are just completing a million pound rebuilding of the clubhouse and it is due to open in a few weeks. He will ask if we want him to.

'Yes please!' we reply.

293

Graham goes on to tell me he has eaten at the club in the past and that the food is excellent. He enjoys playing golf and hopes to join the club at some time. He has played there at different times and likes the course, and the people seem friendly. Whenever he has eaten there he has had a lovely meal.

A couple of days later and we are given the number and name of who to contact. Graham phones and arranges for us to go and see them.

We arrive and after a drink and a chat, we are agreed in principle to having our reception here. The clubhouse is near completion and the setting is perfect. We go home, write a formal application and wait for the committee to approve our request.

A couple of weeks go by and a letter arrives. All ok! Great, we can arrange everything else now.

We have already approached a priest who has agreed to conduct the service and the verger, has agreed to 'verge for free!' so all we need to do is book the church.

Ha! You smell a rat? You are right!

One Sunday after the service, we go into the office to book the church. The vicar is in the office and we ask him if we can book the church for Sunday 25th July for our wedding. He has a grave look on his face, as he draws breath. 'We don't really do weddings on Sundays.' he says. As he looks in the diary he continues, it is also the day of the month we do baptisms in the afternoon as well. His face is serious. Another member of the clergy suggests the baptisms could be incorporated into the morning and evening services, or else they be given a different date. More sharp intakes of breath as the diary is checked. July 25th has no baptisms booked yet. (To be honest, the candidates probably haven't been born yet!)

The vicar is still not happy about us getting married on a Sunday, let alone on an as yet un-booked baptism day. We explain the problem with getting a reception on a Saturday, and our need to fit in with

Graham's fixed holiday. He understands, but is still reluctant. He asks if we can try to change the reception day. He has no problem with any other day, but not a Sunday. He helpfully suggests we have our reception one day, and get married either the day before or after. I may be wrong but I think the look on my face prompted him to withdraw that comment as a bad idea!

We agree to try and change our reception date, and then come back to him.

To say we are disappointed is an understatement. The one thing I had mistakenly taken for granted was the church. I call the priest to tell him and he is equally surprised. The thing is, if he had been in the office at the time there wouldn't have been a problem. We weren't asking the vicar to conduct the service, and although I am aware that at our church weddings do not normally take place on a Sunday, we are regular members of the congregation and more than contribute to the running of the church. Without a congregation there is no church and I find the whole situation hypocritical.

My sister and her partner ring the bells. I act as a server and we all support church functions and activities as well as donate funds and prizes to the twice yearly fairs. We give our time freely and help out whenever we can. I feel really hurt and in that moment I could quite easily never have gone back there again.

Graham was equally upset, not least because of my disappointment.

The issue of baptisms is also something that I get slightly annoyed with. I know everyone has the right to be baptised and I agree with this. The thing that annoys me is that people bring their children to be baptised, they are given advice and information about what it all means and the commitment they are making to God. They agree to bring their child up with good Christian beliefs, but for ninety-nine percent of them they walk out of the church for their bun fight never to be seen again. The next time they probably enter a church is at a wedding or funeral. An odd few turn up for midnight mass, but on the whole, they are never seen again. This is not the child's fault of course, but it's just too easy to say a few words and use the church as a picturesque backdrop for the photos. Chances are, after the service, they won't have any idea of what they have just agreed to.

Added to the fact that as a regular church member we are being asked to step aside to make room for the not-yet-delivered children to be baptised. I am not happy!

They don't even have to pay. Now I know this is controversial, but in my opinion, we have to pay to get married and even be buried, so what's the difference with baptism? Surely we have as much right to a Christian burial with full church honours as we do to enter the Lord's house in the first place? No-one has any problem walloping us with a big bill for having a Christian marriage, or death, (and to be honest, the cost of the former can quite easily bring about the latter!)

So there! That's me on my high horse, and put out!

Later the following week and we are unable to change our reception plans, (mainly because we haven't tried!) Graham agrees to phone the vicar and turn the thumb-screws. I am thankfully out and am glad not to hear the conversation. Graham calls me with the news that the jury is out as the vicar calls other members of the baptism committee to see if they have any objection to cancelling the still non-existent three o'clock baptisms, in favour of our wedding. Graham has reminded him of how we support the church and of how disappointed I will be if we can't get married at All Saints. As our family parish church, I would be mortified.

Ten minutes later and Graham calls me. They have agreed to change the non-existent baptisms and we can have the church. Our wedding date saved, we can now start all the other preparations. Stationery, bridesmaids, flowers, honeymoon, etc.etc.

Planning a wedding according to all accounts is meant to be stressful. Ours will not be!

We can't wait for the day to arrive and everyone associated with us is happy for us too. We don't want to spend a fortune on unnecessary fripperies and want our day to be about our marriage, not our wedding. Having said that we also want the etiquette to be as it should be and we want to enjoy all the planning.

The first thing is to buy a wedding magazine or two. (I am pre, everything on internet here!) Well no more than two, since they weigh a ton and can be recycled as life rafts after use such is their ample bulk! Wading through, I realise a hard hat should come as standard as the mountains of flyers leap out from between the pages as soon as the wrapper is off. Having said that, it gives me all the info I want and a wonderful little flyer about stationery, favours, table furniture and the like. Checking out the cost of stationery though proves a bit of a shocker and again it seems the 'wedding' word increases prices ten-fold. (No Vistaprint around at this time either!)

As I am currently a lady of leisure and since I rather enjoy playing about with my lap-top, I decide to make all our own stationery.

We buy some good quality paper and envelopes and with a nice font, we soon whip up some invitations.

I find a cartoon clip-art picture of a bride and groom which represents very much Graham and me and attach it to the stationery. It all looks great. I am very pleased with myself. With a guest list that seems to get longer by the day, we have soon sent out around one hundred invitations.

Although we are very aware of the way people will ebb and flow throughout our lives, we decide to invite all the people who are close to us at the time of our marriage. We want it to be a celebration of our lives today and as we have managed to escape from the extortionate costs of wedding catering, we can afford to invite all our friends and family.

So, what's next...? Ah the wedding service. We eventually arrange to go through the wedding service. We choose the traditional side of things, along with a couple of readings. We invite two people to read for us, so other than deciding on a couple of hymns, that's that sorted.

With my new found skill in publishing, I set about typing out the whole of the marriage service rather than have half a dozen books and papers flying around.

We also decide that instead of making our vows at the front of the church, we will walk back up the aisle and stand in the middle of the aisle surrounded by our congregation. That means that everyone will be a witness to our vows, and will be able to see and hear us clearly. The idea came from the way the gospel is read in our church. Representing how Jesus spoke to his disciples amidst the throng, it seems a much more intimate way for us to state our vows.

So, with my lap-top producing steam as I type, we are doing really well.

Great, what's next...? Oo, the cake! Jane comes up trumps with this one. 'We'll make one', she declares.

'What?' I reply

'We'll make one, save us some money.' Says Jane. (With the emphasis on 'WE' and 'US' our wedding is definitely becoming a collaborative event.)

'Well, that's o.k. from where you are, I am hopeless at icing cakes' says me.

'Don't worry we'll do it between us. I'll make the cakes and we'll ice them together. We can stack them one on top of the other so we won't need pillars and all the fancy paraphernalia. I'll make it for you as a wedding present!'

'Oh, o.k. actually that's a great idea. We don't really want any gifts, and that would be a good idea for other people. Rather than give us presents, people can do things for us can't they?' I reply.

So next on the list is.... Choir.

Since we are getting married on the first weekend of the industrial fortnight, it seems 90% of the choir are away on holiday. 'No problem,' says my stepmother, 'I'll arrange a choir for you.' She sings in a couple of choirs and in no time has arranged for her church choir to come and sing for us. Great stuff!

Speaking of which we need the organist. Oh bugger! He can't do it as he is playing at his friend's wedding in Stafford. Not to worry though he gives me the name of another young man who will do it for us. So we give him a call and that's that arranged. Just need to sort out the music we want.

Flowers next... Off to the florist and that's sorted as well. I haven't got much idea about what I want, but know that I don't want a great big garden stuck to the front of my dress, and neither do I want a tight bunch of roses. Other than that I am open to suggestions. I look through a few brochures and spot a beautiful bouquet of arum lilies, structured but very open and natural looking, just perfect for my dress. With the small Calla lilies for the boys and a small bunch of arum lilies for the bridesmaids, that's that done. We don't order anything for the church or the reception yet as Jane has another good idea to save money and suggests we do it ourselves. Great idea. We can manage to shove a few flowers in some oasis and pad it out with some greenery from her huge garden. We can make them up in her garage a couple of days before and take them up to the golf club with the cake the day before. Wonderful! Another job done!

So what's left? Something old, new, borrowed and blue.

New, of course, is the dress.

Borrowed and blue, Jane comes up trumps again with her blue garter from when she got married.

Old... Hmm... oh I know, I decide to wear some shoes that I have had for a few years. They are really comfortable and will be lovely with my dress. A goldy-bronze colour. Perfect!

At my next visit to the hairdresser I tell my hairdresser I am getting married!

'No way! I can't believe it! Well don't worry, I'll come and do your hair for you on the day. I don't normally do weddings, but yours will be great fun!' He says.

Oh great, but you don't have to do my hair, honestly, but I'd love you to come to the wedding!'

No honest, I don't mind. You won't be the conventional bride, all boring, we'll grow your hair a bit longer and it'll look better under the veil, and I'll do the bridesmaids for you as a wedding present.

Graham goes slightly pale when I relay the news! He knows I enjoy having my hair done, but basically because every time I have my hair cut I come home with it sticking out from all angles and although he always tells me it looks lovely, he always looks relieved when I have done it and it is a little less wild looking.

As the weeks go by everything takes shape. No stress, just lots of fun and pleasure. I embark on a fitness regime which involves going to the gym around 5 days a week and swimming around three times a week. The weight moves really slowly, but at each fitting for the bridesmaids, I try on the sample dress which becomes a little easier. With the headdress and veil waiting, eventually my dress arrives pristine and beautiful. I try it on...

...Blimey! That's tight! Seems the sample dress is decidedly looser then the new one, back to the diet again!

The bridesmaids' dresses are coming along beautifully. They have all had the same fabric but have chosen different styles. Jane's dress is shrinking rapidly as we near the day, as she is losing weight by the day. Life has become quite stressful for her of late and it's all helping to lose her weight. Not fair! I am struggling to lose every pound and time is running short!

In between all this Kate, who is responsible for the flowers at church, offers to provide some pew-ends, and make some decorations for the reception tables. It saves Jane and me a job although I offer to help her with them.

Christine phones me one day and says, 'I have arranged for someone to come and take us to the church in his nice Jaguar. Hope that's o.k. with you?'

'Lovely,' I reply. How did you do that?'

'Well you met him at one of the Rotary 'do's', and I was telling him about the wedding and he offered to drive over and take us to the church in one of his cars.'

'How lovely! That's very kind of him. We can arrive in style then.'

Next thing. Somewhere to stay on our wedding night. I really don't want to go home, even though we are only up the road from the reception. I want somewhere classy and romantic to stay. We hunt around a bit and arrive at Brockencote Hall. A Georgian country house a few minutes from the reception, it is now a high class French restaurant with around 17 bedrooms, all decorated beautifully. We book 'The Woodpecker room.' It is the best room they have and has a huge four poster bed and a double-ended Jacuzzi-bath. Perfect!

Oh, then there's the honeymoon. Where to go? Long debates as to where to go as we have no strong opinions. The biggest thing is that it's the main two week holiday and everywhere is so expensive. We don't really want to spend thousands on a holiday, and whilst we are musing Dino has a cunning plan... 'Italy'! (What a surprise!!)

With his new job in his uncle's travel company, he believes he has the answer to all our honeymoon requirements.

We decide Italy is not a good idea. We want to go somewhere neutral, that neither of us has ever been before, be it Bognor or Barbados, it is something we feel is important.

After much debate, Dino suggests Sardinia. Still Italian, but as an island off the coast, it is neutral. He sends a web-link, and we peruse the hotel he has in mind. It is set in the rocks high above the coast, with beautiful views. The cuisine is second to none and by all accounts, is pretty spectacular. The price is amazingly low for what is offered, and the only reason for that is due to the fact that it doesn't have a health spa etc. There is another bonus though, the hotel have a cruiser and we get a day trip out on the boat included in the price, meal on board, and get to swim off the coast.

We decide to go ahead so with flights by good-old 'Ryanair' and a taxi to meet and greet us, our honeymoon is booked. Ten days in Sardinia the day after our wedding.

As the wedding gets closer the dress gets a little looser, (well to be honest that's' not quite true, it just gets a little less tight!)

Back to my little lap-top and we have now decided on our hymns and music, so I can type up the wedding service.

Everything is going well, then all of a sudden…disaster! I am typing away happily and things start to change. My computer suddenly goes haywire and goes into safe-mode. Shut it down and start-up again and it starts going wonky again. The words on the screen become huge and then form some sort of 60's psychedelic wallpaper print. What makes it worse is that my sister is at our house and despite me trying to explain that I really need to get this sorted so please excuse me and bear with me whilst I try and save all my work, she ignores me and carries on a conversation that I am unable to join in with and which eventually makes me as crazy as the pictures on my screen.

In one defining moment of non-orgasmic explosion, bang! We both crash at the same time. Computer dies and I slam the lid shut and burst into tears! My sister raises her head slightly and looks bewildered. Completely oblivious to my distress she looks at me as though I have had a slight unseemly aberration, but that it will be overlooked in the interests of politeness.

SHIT! I haven't got anything backed up and it's only three weeks until the wedding.

Still I have now had some lessons learned!

1. Back-up the computer.

2. Back-up the back-up!

3. Learn this lesson before you crash the computer

4. Learn this before you start making wedding stationery for your wedding.

Graham comes home to a scene reminiscent of a war zone after the blast.

'What's the matter?' he asks looking incredulous!'

'Sob, sob, 'computer,' sob, 'broke, wedding,' sob, sob 'crashed,' sob, sob!'

'I think she's got a problem with her computer.' My sister articulates.

'Oh. Dear, well don't worry sweetheart, we'll soon fix it, and if it's going to take some time, well, I'm sure I can arrange for you to come to work and use my work computer. Come on let's make a cup of tea.'

So with red, puffy eyes that's what we do. Once I've calmed down, we arrange for me to go and use Graham's computer at work and start all over again! A few days later it's all done and with the use of the photocopier 120 marriage services are ready to be put together. Crisis over!

Some last minute shopping for a going away outfit, (and a few things to wear whilst we are there, of course) and some accessories, we have only a couple of weeks to go.

The last couple of weeks are busy, but still fun. Life revolves around a calendar, in the middle of which I go for a colonic treatment. Jane-the-Masseuse comes with me for moral support, since it was her idea to go in the first place. I am hoping it may help me to squeeze into the dress a bit easier.

303

LET'S GO FOR A COLONIC!

Jane-the-Masseuse and I have done many holistic courses together over a number of years. We always have fun together and see each other regularly. Jane spends quite a lot of time on the internet and one day phones me full of excitement.

'Guess what I've done?' she cries.

'Well, knowing you Jane, I couldn't even begin to guess, but it's bound to barmy! Go on tell me.'

'I've booked a colonic!'

'What?'

'I've booked a colonic, it's great for you. I've been on-line and looked at loads of web-sites, it's amazing what can stay in your body for years. Apparently it's really good for you.' She tells me excitedly. 'Why don't you come?'

'Hmm, not sure about that.'

'Honestly, it's really good for you, imagine all the rubbish just lying around in your system. It's horrible!'

'Oh all right then. Give me the number and I'll book an appointment and come with you. In for a penny...!'

A few weeks later and off we go for our appointment. By now I am quite looking forward to it. I have also done some research and can't really find anything bad to report. I am sure it will be another experience which will give us something to talk about in the future. I drive and collect Jane and before we know it we are having our colons cleansed together.

A slightly surreal experience as I watch lots of waste from my body flushing down a pipe, but not unpleasant and certainly not painful, which is a relief.

Afterwards I drop Jane off at home and drive home. Half way home I am overwhelmed by tiredness. Arriving home, Graham asks me how I got on and I tell him fine, but that I am so tired I need to go to bed for an hour.

'I'll tell you about it later Gray, I feel like I've been for a long walk in the fresh air. I'm exhausted!'

Fourteen hours late I wake up! I can't believe I have slept for so long. Getting up I feel fantastic! I can't believe it. I can't remember feeling so awake and well in years! I am full of life and energy. Maybe Jane-the-Masseuse was right! I call her.

'How do you feel?' I ask

'Fine, why?'

'I feel fantastic! Can't wait to go back again!'

'Blimey, you've changed your tune!'

'I know. You were right. Maybe we should train to do colonics next term!'

'Yeh, right.' She laughs.

So here we are again. Only I am having a treatment today. Jane is just hand-holding. During my treatment I ask how and where you train to do colonics. The therapist talks in general terms about it, but I persist,

'No really, how do we train to do this?'

'Are you serious?' she asks.

'Absolutely.' I reply. We haven't got any courses lined up for this winter so this would be great to do, wouldn't it Jane.'

'Uh? What? I dunno? If you say so?' Jane is perplexed!

'If you really want to train to do this I can speak to the colonic school for you. I have someone working for me who wants to do it as well. You could all train together and then come and work for me if you like.'

'Really! That would be great.'

'Leave it with me then and I'll get back to you. I think there's a course in September.'

'Great, we'll wait to hear from you.'

Driving back home Jane is still confused. 'We'll never be able to do that.' She says.

'Course we will. We've got the pre-requisites and we've got nothing to do this winter, come on it'll be fun.' I reply

306

'Oh, well if you're sure. I will if you do. Blimey I only meant to have my colon washed. I didn't intend to learn to do it myself!'

'We'll be fine. See what happens anyway, we might not hear anything again.'

MORE WEDDING PLANS

So, only the cake to ice and everything is set! Ah, there's another little tiny hitch. Jane has become increasingly low during the lead-up to the day, and every time I mention 'US' icing the cake, 'WE' don't seem to get very far. Eventually I realise that it's just not going to happen and I will have to use my non-existent cake decorating skills to finish off the cake. Asking several people whether to use royal or fondant icing the majority say fondant. I go to the cake shop and the lady also persuades me that fondant is easy (or more precisely, less difficult!) so armed with apricot jam, marzipan, fondant icing, a few sugar Calla lilies, some wooden dowels to stop all the layers collapsing into one another and lashings of ribbon to hide the mistakes, I set about icing the cake.

The principal is easy. You roll it out really big and then drape it over the cake. It hugs the cake like a glove, (no seams or wrinkles,) then cut off the excess with a sharp knife!

You must be joking!

Eventually I give up. Graham comes to help and give advice, and amazingly we don't cancel the wedding in favour of a cake fight! In the end, we cut out a circle for the top, a long strip for the sides, and between us and a large bottle of vodka, (strictly for sticking the seams together) and a pair of crimpers to make a fancy edge, the cake takes on a new form! We pile them on top of one another and I go off and put the ribbon and flowers on in a darkened room away from prying eyes. With a clay caricature bride and groom to stand pride of place on the top, it looks pretty good. The only thing is, it seems to lean a little to the one side. Never mind, no-one will look too closely at it.

Friday, it's two days before the wedding and another busy day ahead. Graham finishes work early, and while he goes to collect his suit with the boys, I go to the church to do the table arrangements. The organist decides to come and practice the music whilst we are there, and the day becomes an emotional roller-coaster that is truly a surprise.

Listening to him playing the entrance music over and over is absolutely beautiful, and then all of a sudden, he lets out all the stops and the church is filled with a cascade of sound that stops everyone in their tracks, slowly, and without speaking we all wander down the aisle to listen to him play, at the end of which we are all left speechless and with tears in our eyes. It is the perfect start to the next two days, and I am so glad to have heard it, since on the day, it all flashes by in an instant.

Having finished the table decorations for the reception, I head off to Jane's to put them in her garage. On the way over I receive a phone call from Kate the flower lady at church.

'I have got some great news,' she says excitedly, 'I have just seen the flowers for the wedding on Saturday, they must have spent a couple of thousand pounds on them, and the good news is we can leave them there until Sunday so you can have them! There is a huge decoration on the font, flowers either side of the church door, window arrangements and a couple of freestanding decorations, as well as the pew-ends! They are in neutral colours so will look fantastic for your wedding!'

I am so excited and feel quite emotional. I call at the florist afterwards and walk in telling them all about my inherited flowers when all of a sudden, I stop mid-sentence. Suddenly I am aware of the amount of flowers in the shop. Buckets full of Calla and Arum lilies are all over the shop. 'Are these mine?' I ask.

'Yes, all of them!' she replies.

'They are beautiful' I say.

'We could have sold them ten times over. Everyone who has seen them wants them.' She says.

My eyes fill with tears. I am really overwhelmed by it all.

So there we are, all set and raring to go. Two days to go and all set. We go and collect the dresses, take them to Jane's, and in the evening she has a party for us. Graham and me, Chrissy and her partner, Jane and her family, and Dino, who has just arrived back. He insists on going to stay at his cousin's in Kidderminster afterwards and at the end of the evening, a little worse for a few drinks, Jane and I go upstairs to try on my dress.

Having been under strict instructions by the bridal shop to guard it with our lives and believing that even looking at it may make it crinkle into some uncontrollable heap, we throw caution to the wind and dance around her bedroom with the dress flowing behind billowing and carefree.

After our moment of madness, we carefully put it back on the hanger, drape it over the chair, as instructed and creep back downstairs like naughty children.

Graham and I wander home, happy and excited and looking forward to the next day.

Saturday, Andrea and Mario are arriving. We go to fetch them from New Street station. Andrea is six months pregnant but is blooming, and after hugs and kisses we head off home. Dropping their luggage at our house, we take the cars to drop one off Brockencote Hall where we are to spend our wedding night, and all squeeze into the little Ford Ka after a cup of afternoon tea.

Later that evening we head off to West Bromwich for a meal with Christine and her partner, Jane and Jodie, Little Mario, Andrea and Mario, and two of Christine's neighbours who are putting up the overseas guests overnight. Dino is invited but decides not to come as he wants to spend time with his cousins.

I am starting to become irritated with Dino. Graham has asked him to be a best man. He has two, his son and Dino. Leading up to the wedding, Dino has been rather unreliable. Despite him being in Italy, which is not

311

a problem, whenever I have asked when he is coming over, how will he get from the airport, which flight will he be catching, and how long will he stay afterwards he has been evasive.

Eventually, when he arrives, he turns up in Kidderminster! We have made plans for him to stay in West Bromwich overnight arranged transport to get him there and booked him a meal with everyone. Having turned up at Jane's party late, although he is very entertaining, he refuses our offer of staying with us and also refuses to come for the meal in West Brom, saying he 'has to spend some time with his cousins!' He says he will make his own way to the church!

I am cross but on the other hand cannot care less. He is not important enough in our wedding day to matter. If he fails to turn up we can manage very happily without him, and if he wants to find his own way there, good luck to him! I do think, however, he is rather rude to spend so much time with his relatives, (especially as when he stayed before they were hardly joined at the hip!) since the whole purpose of his trip is to come to our wedding, and he seems to want to spend very little time with us beforehand. Hey-ho, whatever! As long as Graham, me, the vicar and two witnesses are there I really couldn't care less. It is our day and I refuse to let anyone spoil it in any way.

We spend a lovely evening having a meal with friends and leave early to drop off the boys, whilst Christine and I drive back home for an early night.

Before we leave, Graham takes me for a little walk along the road, and takes my hand. He turns to me and says to me,

'Will you marry me?'

'Yes please' I reply.

'If you change your mind at the altar, just say so, and we can turn around and walk out together. I will still love you just as much, and we can live together just the same. I don't want you to do anything you don't want to, or have any regrets.'

'Graham, I can't wait to marry you. Thank you for asking, but don't worry, God willing, I will see you at the altar tomorrow. I love you so much.'

We have a hug and a kiss and then say goodnight.

Christine and I drive home, and I finish off some music to play during the reception before going to bed, during which Chrissy and I talk and my phone rings.

Dino!

'Ignore it' Christine says. So I do!

I realise there have been several missed calls from him during the evening, which I haven't heard.

A while later it rings again. I ignore it again!

We decide to teach him a bit of a lesson and turn my phone onto silent! Hopefully he may become a little agitated or inconvenienced as he doesn't have the address of the church. I will ring him tomorrow and tell him the address.

We head off to bed and sleep really well...

25TH JULY 2004

We wake around 9.00am. It's our wedding day! I am really excited but very calm. I am exceedingly happy and want to enjoy every moment of it!

I have breakfast and a cup of tea before having a shower. A little later, my hairdresser arrives with his girlfriend, followed by Jane and Jodie. We open a bottle of champagne and have a drink before getting ready to head off to Christine's.

After a while Jane's phone rings. It's Dino! Oh heavens, I forgot to turn my phone off silent, and have also forgotten to call him with instructions of where to go!

I check my phone, 17 missed calls! All from Dino!

Jane gives him details of where to go before reporting to us that he has caught the train from Kidderminster to Smethwick Galton Bridge, got into a taxi, and told the driver to go to West Bromwich. They had been driving around for about 45 minutes trying to find Christine's house! He kept telling the driver,

'I need to get to Christine's house, her partner, he is a lawyer, you must know them, we are getting married today!'

Amazingly the driver took pity on him and drove around whilst Dino frantically tried calling me before finding he had Jane's mobile and struck lucky!

Serves him right! They say revenge is a dish better served cold! 'I am agree with this!' as Dino used to say.

After we all have a good laugh at this, we make a move to leave. I go with my hairdresser to show him and his girlfriend the way. This is the only time I feel rather nervous during the whole day, as his girlfriend is driving rather more quickly than I am comfortable with and I pray like mad that I get over to West Bromwich safely and arrive in one piece at the church! Thankfully we all arrive and after Christine phoning ahead to make sure all the guests who are staying at the neighbour's house across the road are out of sight, including Graham who has moved across the road as well, we are soon in Christine's house with all our things and can relax until it is time to get ready.

The plan is for the girls to get ready at Christine's and the boys to get ready at the neighbour's.

The lady neighbour arrives with a couple of platefuls of tuna sandwiches and we tuck in with another glass of champagne to wash it all down with!

Time arrives to get ready, and we all pile upstairs to Christine's bedroom. We are just ready to take it in turns to use the bathroom, when her partner arrives. He disappears into the bathroom and doesn't come out for ages! We are stuck in the bedroom half clothed getting rather warm, and we wait, and wait and wait!

We can't get dressed or do our make-up until he comes out, and time is ticking along! We are all developing a less-then-rosy glow and although we are all a little irritated he couldn't have got ready earlier or gone across the road, none of us are brave enough to tell him to get a move on!

I go downstairs to get my hair done. By now my driver has arrived with the car. Both he and my hairdresser are amazed by how calm and relaxed I am!

'Aren't you nervous?' thee driver asks.

'Nervous? Why would I be nervous?

'Well, you know how people get flustered on their wedding day'

'Naaa, I just want to enjoy it!'

'But look at the time and you're not dressed yet!'

'Tell me about it! We are waiting for himself to vacate the bathroom!'

'Will you have enough time?'

'Gosh yes, we've got half an hour, I've only got to have a wash, put my make-up on, and then put my dress on, it will only take 20 minutes!'

'You're amazing!' he says.

'That's why I offered to do her hair' my hairdresser says. 'She's not like normal people, I don't normally do weddings, but Gill's is going to be a real laugh!'

'I'll take that as a complement!' I reply.

I go back upstairs and as Christine's partner finally vacates the bathroom, we run in, in turn, to have a wash and brush-up, do our make up and put on our dresses.

By now we are all becoming rather hot as we can't have the door open as he is still about! I squeeze into the corset they have given me and stuff the chicken fillets under my boobs. Jane zips me in and I am ready!

Well, almost!

'Blimey this is tight!' I look in the mirror and can see the outline of the corset underneath. 'This dress is never a twelve! It's smaller than the one in the shop. It's no good, I can't wear this corset. Let's take it off!'

So a quick undo and I am zipped back into my dress minus the corset.

'Much better!' No bra either but I shove the chicken fillets in to give me a bit of uplift! 'They can't go far as there is no room to move anything in this dress!'

So that's it, we are ready. Jane and Jodie go down first, and then Christine and I follow.

We check the boys have all gone and go outside. The neighbours are twitching the curtains and a few are out watching.

Christine takes me to one side. 'Now Gilly, I have to ask you, like Dad would have done. Are you sure you want to marry Graham?' She asks very seriously.

'Yes, definitely!' I reply with a serious smile.

We go outside and look at the time. It's 3.05pm. I have told my Godmother I will call at her house on the way to the church which is about a mile up the road. I think that by the time our driver has taken Jane and Jodie to church and come back for Christine and me, we won't have much time to call at my Godmother's.

My Godmother has been the most amazing woman in the world to me all of my life, and especially after my mum died just before my 18th birthday. She has wiped my tears, fed me, given me more worldly advice that I could wish for and is the wisest person I have ever met. I couldn't possibly have got married without seeing her on my most special day.

So I say 'Shall we all go together?'

'What do you mean?' the driver says.

'Well I want to call at my Godmother's on the way so it would be better if we all go together.'

'Are you sure? It will be a bit squashed!'

'Don't worry, it's only just up the road, we'll be fine.'

'Sure?'

'Absolutely, it will save you fighting your way back around the block!'

'You really are relaxed aren't you?'

'Why wouldn't I be, it's a happy day. Come on let's go.'

The other three squeeze in the back and I bundle myself and my dress and what seems like a massive bouquet into the front seat. We head off and call at my Godmother's where we all bundle out again and stand on the lawn whilst she takes some photographs. More neighbours come out to wave us off as we all pile back into the car again and head off up to church.

We pull up outside the church and I look left towards the church door. The boys are outside. I catch a glimpse of Graham having a last cigarette (typical!) before someone spots us and moves them hastily inside. We get out of the car and stand on the pavement in front of the lych-gate.

The photographer takes a couple of photos as my driver ducks down to hold my train down with his fingertips. Then we walk up to the door where we are met by the vicars who are conducting the service.

We are slightly early after all the rushing about, so we have a little chat, straighten my dress and Christine pops to the toilet. The vicar says, 'Well, if you're ready, shall we start?'

'Yes please' I respond and with a nod and a wink, the organ strikes up, and with Christine on my left, Jane on my right and Jodie behind, we walk down the aisle to meet my soon-to-be-husband.

This is the moment I have really looked forward to. I have played it over and over in my mind, the sound of the music, the anticipation of the whole congregation, the big girly moment of showing off in my big dress and looking down the aisle to see Graham waiting for me. It lives up to all my expectations and the moment is gone just as quickly as I knew it would.

We come to a stop and Graham steps over to me and looks at me for the first time. (He tells me later that he didn't dare turn to look at me before as he knew he would either cry, or run down the aisle to meet me and as he couldn't trust himself not to do either he stayed still!)

As we have the introduction, Graham turns to me and whispers, 'You have never looked more beautiful than you do right now.'

We continue the service and I sing my heart out at the hymns. The choir is fantastic, and the organ lets out the stops!

As we come to the vows, we turn and walk down to the middle of the aisle and exchange our vows, and rings. There is an audible intake of breath from the congregation as we agree to 'obey' one another, and we are then proclaimed 'husband and wife!'

We go off to sign the register, and listen to the choir sing. There is a pause as the organist and singer move to the back of the church to sing "O Mio Babbino Caro." Then as she starts to sing she loses her pitch and stops.

Clearing her throat, she says to the organist, 'Can we start again please?'

319

They start again and the tension in the church makes the whole thing electrifying. Everyone is willing her to get through it unscathed, and she does so magnificently!

Deserved applause follows.

We move on to the blessing and then finally, we hear the organ strike up again to Rondo in G by John Bull.

And so, ten months and nine days after a chance meeting on the corner of the street, we head off down the aisle as husband and wife, Mr and Mrs Graham Edwards.

I have never been so happy in my entire life...

Outside we stand and chat a little as people give us keepsakes and take photographs. The weather has held so far and although it is a little grey overhead, the day is bright and in our hearts and minds it is gloriously sunny.

A change of location for all the guests and we arrive at the reception. The weather has cleared up and we pose for lots of photos. Graham and I are moved inside for a photo with the cake. The photographer lines us up, gets his shot ready, moves his head from side-to-side, and says 'Is this cake straight?'

'Don't worry, just take the photo, no-one will notice when it's printed!'

We have a wonderful meal and then the speeches start. Christine leads us off with an opening line that brings the house down! Jane follows with a seamless performance. Graham is then rendered speechless, as everyone has stolen his lines! I thank everyone almost endlessly, especially Ann for not complaining about the food! (One of her hobbies!)

The rest of the reception goes by in a whirl and before we know it we are all leaving. Chris and her partner take us off to Brokencote Hall for our first night as Mr and Mrs Edwards. We are taken to out bridal suite which is beautiful. The Woodpecker room. A huge four poster bed with an en-suite containing an equally huge double ended bath. Graham turns on the taps, pours in the bubble-bath and I get in one end as he passes me a glass of chilled champagne and gets in the other end.

Five minutes later, I have sipped half my glass, and suddenly say, 'Gray, you'll have to get me out!'

His face lights up! 'What, already?'

'Yes please.'

He leaps out with a grin from ear to ear. He holds up a towel, and has to haul me out of the bath. I stagger into his arms and say, 'I'm really sorry, I need to go to bed.'

'Yes, yes, come on then.'

'No, I mean I'm exhausted!'

He helps me into bed and covers me over with the bedclothes.

'I'm really sorry, Gray, I'm exhausted. I need to go to sleep!' And with that I conk out!

Waking up the next morning, Graham makes me a cup of tea and then picks up my wedding dress and starts looking inside it.

'What are you doing?'

'I'm looking to see if I can get a refund!'

'Cheeky!' We start to get ready to go to breakfast.

Looking around the room for the suit carrier I have put our going away clothes into, I discover it's missing!

I phone Christine. Eventually she finds it on the back seat of her car! She offers to bring it over, but as we are more or less passing her door en-route to the airport, we decide to call in on the way.

We eat breakfast and make haste to leave. We are both really tired and start to think it might have been a good idea to have spent our first day leisurely waking, eating and relaxing. Too late now though, so off we go and 45 minutes later we are at Christine's. Graham makes a quick change and goes outside for a cigarette and I change into my new suit complete with accessories. Black skirt and pink jacket. Simple, but really classy. I walk out of the house and everyone is out there to wave us off and it provides a lovely send-off to our honeymoon.

We arrive at Stansted airport, and no sooner are we on the plane than Graham is asleep. Next stop is Sardinia and ten days of relaxation and sunshine.

I remember that after we had decided to get engaged I prayed really hard that we would get to our wedding day safely and have the perfect end to my very own fairytale story.

I am not disappointed. I say a little prayer of thanks for such a lovely wedding and the best start to married life we could possibly wish for...

Thank You For Reading An Ordinary Woman.

I hope this will be the first of several books about me
and my life, and I hope you enjoy reading them.
If you do, please write a review on Amazon or Amazon
Kindle or when you finish it.

Gillian Xx